FAITH CHRISTIAN SCHOOL
P.O. BOX 1280 HWY. 50 & HARRIS RD.
WILLIAMS BAY, WI 53191
(414) 245-9404

Reading

for Christian Schools® 3-1

Bob Jones University Press, Greenville, South Carolina 29614

Consultants

from the administration and faculty of Bob Jones University

Grace C. Collins, Ph.D., *Chairman, Department of Linguistics*
Walter G. Fremont, Ed.D., *Dean of the School of Education*
Melva M. Heintz, M.A., *Elementary Principal*
Janice A. Joss, M.A.T., *Graduate School of Education*
Betty Anne Rupp, M.A., *Professor of Reading, School of Education*
Philip D. Smith, Ed.D., *Provost*
Hazel M. Truman, M.A., *Project Director, University Press*

READING for Christian Schools ® 3-1

Produced in cooperation with the Bob Jones University School of Education and Bob Jones Elementary School.

ISBN 0-89084-221-3

©1983 Bob Jones University Press
Greenville, South Carolina 29614

"Whistles." Reprinted from *Here, There, and Everywhere* published by Minton, Balch, and Co. The editors searched diligently to find the source and to obtain permission to use this poem, but without success.

Harper and Row, Publishers, Inc. "Jim" from *Bronzeville Boys and Girls* by Gwendolyn Brooks. Copyright 1956 by Gwendolyn Brooks Blakely. Reprinted by permission of Harper & Row, Publishers, Inc.

Houghton Mifflin Company: Glossary material based on the lexical database of the *Children's Dictionary,* copyright ©1981 Houghton Mifflin Company. No part of this book may be reproduced or transmitted in any form or by any means, electronic or mechanical, including photocopying and recording, or by any information storage or retrieval system, except as may be expressly permitted by the 1976 Copyright Act or with prior written permission from both Houghton Mifflin Company and the Bob Jones University Press.

20   19   18   17   16   15   14   13   12

CONTENTS

MAKING MELODY

SPECIAL DEEDS

DAYS TO REMEMBER

MAKING MELODY

Grandma Tildy's Music

Creak, crick, creak, crick!

It was Monday. Grandma Tildy rocked back and forth. Her hands knitted the wool faster than a boy could reel in a fish.

"This will make a nice winter hat for Sammy," she thought, smiling to herself. She hummed a little tune to the rhythm of her rocker.

Creak, crick.

On Tuesday Grandma Tildy took the hat to Sammy. Creaky, squeak, creaky, squeak. Grandma Tildy's old brown shoes squeaked a song with every step she took.

Creaky, squeak.

Whirr and ping, whirr and ping.

It was Wednesday. Grandma Tildy sat at her old sewing machine. Her hands nimbly sewed a seam here and a tuck there, a dart here and a hem there.

"This will make a nice dress for Mrs. Hopper's new baby," she thought, smiling to herself. She hummed a little tune as she sewed.

Whirr and ping.

On Thursday Grandma Tildy took the baby dress to Mrs. Hopper. Creaky, squeak, creaky, squeak. Grandma Tildy's old brown shoes squeaked a song with every step she took.

Creaky, squeak.

Click-a-click-a-click.

It was Friday. Grandma Tildy stirred and mixed, patted and rolled. She made ten pies—four apple, two pumpkin, three cherry, and one banana.

"My friends will like these pies," she thought, smiling and humming a little tune.

Click-a-click.

Click-a-click.

On Saturday Grandma Tildy delivered the pies. Creaky, squeak, creaky, squeak. Her old brown shoes had a lot of singing to do that day!

Creaky, squeak.

Did Grandma Tildy's shoes rest on Sunday? No sir! Creaky, squeak, creaky, squeak. Down to the little white church they took Grandma Tildy.

Creaky, squeak.

At the church the townspeople gathered around
Grandma Tildy. "We love you, Grandma Tildy.
You are so good to us!" They hugged her; they
kissed her; they said nice things to her. Everyone
loved Grandma Tildy.

Everyone, that is, except Mrs. Upjohn.
"Hmmph!" she said, sticking her nose in the air.
"Who does she think she is?"

On Monday Mrs. Upjohn went to the Smiths'
house.

On Tuesday Mrs. Upjohn went to the Littles'
house.

On Wednesday Mrs. Upjohn went to the Hays'
house.

On Thursday Mrs. Upjohn went to the Frankes'
house.

On Friday Mrs. Upjohn went to the Blands'
house.

Every place she went, she said the same thing.

"You know, Grandma Tildy does nice things," she would say. Then, cupping her hand to her mouth and lowering her voice, she would go on. "But the creak, crick of her rocking chair, the whirr and ping of her sewing machine, and the click-a-click of her eggbeater are disturbing this town. That awful creaky, squeak of her shoes and the little tune she hums upset everyone. How selfish she is to make such noise! There is no peace and quiet when Grandma Tildy is around. It ought not to be allowed."

The townspeople stopped to listen to Mrs. Upjohn. The creak, crick, the whirr and ping, and the click-a-click began to bother them. But it was the creaky, squeak and the little tune that really got under their skin.

"Grandma Tildy," they said at last, "you must stop rocking and sewing. You must not use the eggbeater. And do not, do *not* wear those old shoes and hum. There is no peace and quiet when you are around."

Grandma Tildy looked at the people sadly. She went into her house and shut the door. The people of Pottstown listened. They did not hear creak, crick, whirr and ping, or click-a-click. They did not hear creaky, squeak or the little tune.

"Good!" said Mrs. Upjohn. "Now we will have peace and quiet."

Monday passed. There was no sound from Grandma Tildy's house.

Tuesday passed. Still there was no sound.

On Wednesday the townspeople began to gather. "Do you think Grandma Tildy is all right?"

Mrs. Upjohn snorted. "She's just miffed, that's all."

On Thursday people began to stroll past Grandma Tildy's house, hoping to hear *something*, at least.

On Friday the people began to talk.

"It would be good to hear Grandma Tildy's rocker going creak, crick."

"Or her sewing machine saying whirr and ping."

"Even the sound of her eggbeater would satisfy me."

Mrs. Upjohn started to speak. "But the peace and . . ." The people of Pottstown looked hard at her, and Mrs. Upjohn didn't finish her sentence.

Early on Saturday all of Pottstown was gathered at Grandma Tildy's door, except Mrs. Upjohn.

"Grandma Tildy!" they called. "We would like to hear your rocker go creak, crick."

The door opened a crack.

"We would very much like to hear your sewing machine go whirr and ping and your eggbeater go click-a-click."

The door opened wider.

"But most of all, we would like to hear the creaky, squeak of your shoes and your little tune. Those sounds are like music to our ears."

The door flew open!
All day the people of
Pottstown listened to the
creak, crick,
whirr and ping,
and click-a-click
coming from Grandma
Tildy's house. They
listened, and they smiled.

The next day was
Sunday. Creaky, squeak,
creaky, squeak. Grandma
Tildy was on her way to
church. She had a new
scarf for Tommy, a
birthday cake for Susie,
and a pretty new apron
for Mrs. Upjohn.

"Hooray!" shouted the
people.

Creaky, squeak!

Trumpets and Pitchers

Because Israel had turned from God, He sent the powerful Midianite army to trouble them. Judges 6 and 7 tell the story of the godly young man chosen by God to lead Israel back to Himself and then to victory against the enemy.

Gideon's Trumpet Call

Gideon stopped to rest. He looked at the pile of wheat left to thresh. He dared not rest long. The wheat must be threshed and hidden from the enemy. Then Gideon's family would have wheat to make into bread. They would not go hungry. Gideon stretched and looked around. No one was in sight.

He walked back to the piles of wheat hidden by the winepress.

As he passed an oak tree, a voice said, "The Lord is with you. You are a brave man."

Gideon turned around quickly. He peered into the shadows under the tree. "The Lord has forsaken us and given us into the hands of the enemy," Gideon said quietly.

"You will save your people from the enemy. Have I not sent you?" the man said.

"Please do not go away," said Gideon.

He ran to prepare an offering. He made some cakes and sacrificed a goat. Gideon brought his offering back to the oak tree. Carefully he placed it on a rock. The man held out his staff, and the sacrifice burst into flames. Then Gideon knew that this man was an angel of the Lord.

Gideon stepped back and fell to his knees, but the angel of the Lord had left as suddenly as he had come.

That same night the Lord spoke to Gideon again. He told Gideon to destroy his father's altar and to cut down the idols beside it. He told Gideon to make an altar to the Lord God.

But Gideon feared the people of his father's household and of the city. They would be angry if he cut down their idols. So Gideon waited. After dark, he took ten servants and slipped out to do as God commanded.

In the morning a huge crowd gathered. "Who did this?" the people murmured. "Who cut down our idols?"

"It was Gideon," someone called.

The crowd rushed to Gideon's house. "Send Gideon out," they shouted. "We will kill him!"

Gideon's father opened the door. "Will you plead for your idols?" he asked. "If your idols are so great, let them plead for themselves. Those who worship them should be killed. They have sinned against the Lord God."

Not far away in the Valley of Jezreel, Gideon watched the enemy gather. They came from the east and from the south. Their tents filled the valley.

Gideon took out his trumpet and blew a call to war. Men came to join him.

Other men ran with the news to far-off places. They told how Gideon had destroyed the idols and planned to fight the enemy. Soon an army of men came to help Gideon.

Then Gideon talked to God again. He wanted the army to see that God would give them the victory. He wanted to know that he was doing just as God wanted.

"Will You save Your people as You have said?" he asked. "I will put a sheepskin on the ground. If it is wet with dew and the ground is dry, then I will know You are going to save Your people."

Gideon set the sheepskin on the ground. Then he went to bed. When morning came, Gideon hurried to check the sheepskin. The ground was dry all around the sheepskin, but the sheepskin glistened and sparkled in the morning sunlight. It started to drip as Gideon lifted it. He wrung a bowlful of water out of it!

Gideon prayed again. "Do not be angry," he said, "but once more show Your power. This time let the sheepskin be dry and the ground be wet with dew."

Gideon left the sheepskin out again. The night stretched on and on.

When the first light of morning shone, Gideon sprang up to check the sheepskin. He ran through the wet grass and scooped the sheepskin up. It was dry! The Lord God was going to save his people from the enemy.

The Battle of the Lord

As the army marched, the Lord spoke to Gideon. "The people are too many. They will think they have won the battle themselves. Tell those who are afraid of the battle to go home."

Gideon followed the Lord's command. Twenty-two thousand men admitted they were afraid and went home. Only ten thousand men stayed.

Then the Lord spoke to Gideon again. "There are still too many people," He said.

Gideon took the army to get a drink at a stream. The men had marched for days on hot, dusty roads. They were tired and thirsty. Many of them fell on their knees or bent over to drink the cool water.

Others scooped up handfuls of water and lapped it like thirsty dogs. They watched the hills for the enemy as they drank the cool water.

"Keep the ones that lapped the water," said the Lord. "Send the others home."

Only three hundred men had lapped the water. Gideon's army looked very, very small.

That night Gideon and his servant crept down to the Valley of Jezreel. The enemy covered the valley like a swarm of grasshoppers. Even their camels were too many to be counted.

"Our army is so small," whispered Gideon. "The enemy has many more men than we have."

The servant touched Gideon's arm and pointed. Two men were walking toward them. Gideon and his servant stepped behind some rocks and stood very still. The men kept on walking and talking.

"I dreamed a dream," one said. "A huge cake of barley bread tumbled into our camp and was crushed flat. Look, my hands are still shaking. It was an awful nightmare."

The other man shook his head in despair. "That barley cake must mean Gideon. His God will deliver us into his hand."

Gideon and his servant slipped quietly away. "The Lord God is fighting for us. Hurry, let us wake up our army," Gideon said.

Quickly Gideon prepared the army. Each man was given a trumpet and an empty pitcher. Bright torches were placed inside the pitchers.

Gideon's voice rang out over the camp. "Look at me!" he commanded. "When we come to the camp of the enemy, do as I do."

Then all was silent except the tramp, tramp, tramp of marching feet. The little army surrounded the camp. The dark night hid the waiting men well.

Gideon blew his trumpet mightily. The army took up the sound, each man on his own trumpet. Gideon broke his pitcher and let his torch shine. The army broke their pitchers. All the torches shone! The enemy camp was circled by a ring of fire!

Gideon shouted. The army shouted with him. But not one man lifted a hand to fight.

The Lord confused the enemy. They began to fight each other. They fled back and forth within the camp.

Gideon and his men watched as the enemy began to flee. "Look," called Gideon. "The enemy army is running away! The Lord God has saved His people!"

Then Gideon raised his trumpet again. He blew another loud blast.

Together Gideon and his men ran toward the enemy camp.

Together they chased out the last of the enemy.

Oh, sing unto the Lord a new song; for he hath done marvellous things: his right hand, and his holy arm, have gotten him the victory.

Psalm 98:1

A Strange Instrument

Mr. Martin lived in Florida, not in Scotland, but he found a way to bring Scottish music into his house by learning to play a very unusual instrument. This is a true story about a man who praises the Lord with his music.

The Scottish March

Mr. Martin picked up the small black pipe he had brought home. It had a row of little holes on one side and one more hole in the back. Mr. Martin blew a low note on the pipe.

Rob sat up. "What's that, Dad?" he asked.

Mr. Martin handed the pipe to Rob. "This is called a *practice chanter*. Would you like to try to play a tune?" he asked.

Rob puffed hard. Not a sound would come out.

"Just blow softly," Mr. Martin said.

Rob tried again. This time he blew too softly, and it sounded like a quacking duck.

"A chanter teaches you the notes to play on the bagpipes," Mr. Martin explained. "If you learn to play this practice chanter, I'll get a set of bagpipes for you."

"You will?" Rob asked. "Then I'll try my best. I would like to play the bagpipes."

October passed, then November. The nights became colder.

Rob and his father played the practice chanter almost every night. Their fingers flew up and down the pipe. Soon the notes began to sound like the Scottish marching song they were learning to play.

Winter came. At Christmas Mrs. Martin
watched as Rob and his father opened two boxes
that looked just alike. Inside each box lay an
odd-shaped bag with five long pipes sticking out.
One of the pipes looked just like the chanter they
had been using.

Rob picked up his bagpipe and began huffing
and puffing on the blowpipe. Every now and then
the pipes let out a squeal.

Mrs. Martin laughed. "Have you trapped a
baby pig in there?" she asked.

Mr. Martin filled his bag with air. Soon it
looked as fat as a little piglet.

Rob and Mr. Martin leaned the three long pipes against their upper arms and shoulders. With both hands, they held the pipe chanters that were connected to their bagpipes.

Mr. Martin nodded, and together they played a note. A loud screech rattled the windows. Mrs. Martin held her ears.

"Wait," Mr. Martin said. "I think the pipes and chanters need to be tuned to each other."

He adjusted the reeds one by one until a clear pitch sounded. Rob watched, then tuned his the same way. He tested his chanter. Quick as a wink, the reed in the longest pipe slipped into the bag.

Rob tried to peek inside, but it was as dark as night. He turned the bagpipes upside down and shook them, but the reed had disappeared.

Mr. Martin chuckled and lifted Rob's bagpipes. Soon he had found the spot where the reed lay in the bag. He slipped it back into the stock and then shook it. At last it fell out.

Rob tuned his pipe again.

"Okay. Let's play," Mr. Martin said.

"If my reed slips into the bag this time, I'm going to glue it into place!" Rob said with a smile.

At last they could play the Scottish march they had learned on the small practice chanter.

Gospel Songs

The Martins decided to send Rob to a Christian school. One Sunday morning they visited the church where Rob would go to school. On Sunday night they went back again. They had never heard the gospel before.

The next week they hurried back to church. That night the pastor asked if anyone wanted to be saved. The Martins walked to the front of the church. They needed to be saved. They bowed their heads and asked Christ to save them.

After that the Martins started to read the Bible. One day Mr. Martin opened his Bible to Psalm 40:3. It said, "And he hath put a new song in my mouth, even praise unto our God; many shall see it and fear, and shall trust in the Lord."

Mr. Martin closed his Bible. "I am going to use my bagpipes to praise the Lord."

Mr. Martin whistled the tune of one of the new songs he had learned at church.

Suddenly he stopped. "I could play that," he said to himself. He hurried to get his bagpipes. Quickly he filled the bag with air, tuned the pipes and chanter, and started to play.

The sound of bagpipes filled the house.

Rob dashed into the room. "That's a song from church," he exclaimed.

Mr. Martin kept on playing. He didn't mix up any of the notes. At last he finished and set the bagpipes down.

"Where did you get the music for that gospel song?" Rob asked.

Mr. Martin smiled. "I just played it. I played the notes as I remembered them."

Mr. Martin could not find gospel music written for the bagpipes, so he learned many gospel songs by playing the notes as he remembered them. His pastor found out about his bagpipe gospel songs. He asked Mr. Martin to play some of them in church.

The next Sunday night Mr. Martin wore his kilt to church. After the singing ended, the pastor called on Mr. Martin to play.

Before he began, Mr. Martin quoted Psalm 40:3. "And he hath put a new song in my mouth, even praise unto our God: many shall see it, and fear, and shall trust in the Lord." Then he said, "I want to use my bagpipes to praise the Lord. I hope someone will trust in the Lord and be saved just as I was. Then he will have a new song too."

Mr. Martin began to play. His bagpipes hummed each word of its new song. Mr. Martin had found a way to praise the Lord with his bagpipes.

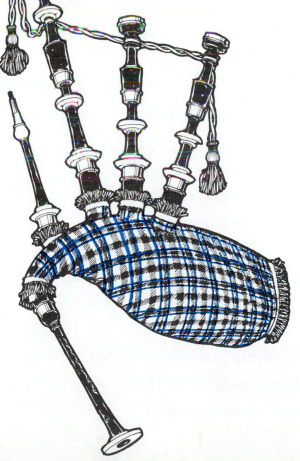

The Singing Knight

Sir Bryan

Long, long ago and far, far away there lived a brave and handsome knight named Sir Bryan. He wore shining armor and rode on a sleek, white horse named Charger. Together they rode into battle with Sir Bryan holding his long spear before him.

Charger would arch his neck and prance forward proudly whenever Sir Bryan gave a command.

> Then away he would race,
> faster than sunlight,
> his mane flowing,
> his eyes glowing.

Now Sir Bryan could fight just as bravely as any knight in the whole kingdom. He had done many brave and knightly deeds.

But still, the other knights did not admire or praise him. They would look his way and laugh. They hardly ever spoke to him.

Sometimes all the bold knights paraded through a town after a battle. The lovely ladies leaned out their windows. They cheered the brave knights.

When the ladies saw Sir Bryan parading by, they started to cheer him too. But suddenly, one after the other, they opened their eyes wide and gasped. Then they giggled so hard that they had to hold their scarves over their mouths. Then they turned away from Sir Bryan. They tossed their flowers at the feet of the other knights.

The awful truth was that Sir Bryan was different from every other knight. Everyone could see it, even when he had on his whole suit of armor. For Sir Bryan always carried with him a long-necked, stringed lute. And everyone knew that no one who claimed to be a brave knight ever played any sort of a musical instrument. Music was only played by bards and jesters!

So no matter how bravely Sir Bryan fought, no one admired him. They only laughed at him because of his lute.

One day Sir Bryan rode Charger deep into the forest. When he reached a clearing he said, "This is where we will stop, Charger. I will play my lute in this quiet place."

Sir Bryan sat cross-legged in the grass. He strummed his lute and hummed a sad song to himself.

Charger contentedly munched the grass nearby.
Every once in a while he lifted his head and
whinnied. He sounded as if he felt sad for his
master.

"Ah, Charger, my dear friend," Sir Bryan
sighed. "I wish you could tell me what to do. I
wish people would understand. A knight truly can
be a brave knight and like music too. There is
really nothing wrong with putting the two
together."

The light, shimmery music of Sir Bryan's lute
always made him feel a little better. For a while
he just strummed and hummed.

"Well, Charger," he finally said, "I know that I
won't give up my lute. So there's just one thing
left to do. I must leave this land. I must find
another land where I can play my lute and be a
knight too."

Sir Bryan swung up onto Charger's back. "I have to tell the king before I leave," he said. "I have to ask him to let me travel to a distant land."

So off Charger galloped,
faster than sunlight,
his mane flowing,
his eyes glowing.

Sir Bryan and Groggle

As Sir Bryan came to the center of town, he saw that the townspeople were in a flurry. A messenger was blowing a horn.

"Hear ye! Hear ye!" the messenger shouted. "The fair Princess Millicent has been captured by the giant, Groggle. Any brave and handsome knight who can rescue her will receive a reward. He will be given whatever his heart desires! Hear ye! Hear ye!"

Sir Bryan's heart leaped up within him. His one desire was to be loved and respected by the people of this land. He would fight a giant for that.

Without wasting a moment, Sir Bryan started the quest to rescue Princess Millicent.

Away Charger raced
faster than sunlight,
his mane flowing,
his eyes glowing.

Sir Bryan arrived at the giant's cave long before any of the other knights. Groggle had the lovely Princess Millicent tied to a rock near one side of the cave. He was ranting and raving and throwing things as only a giant can do.

Sir Bryan reached for his dagger. He reached
too far, and his hand plucked a few strings of his
lute by mistake. When Groggle heard the music,
he turned around to listen. Sir Bryan strummed
the lute again. Groggle stood still.

34

"It seems that Groggle likes music," Sir Bryan called to Princess Millicent. "Perhaps he is smarter than I thought."

Princess Millicent was too frightened to reply. Sir Bryan kept his eyes on the giant. He put his dagger next to him where he could easily reach it. Then he took his lute and sat cross-legged on Groggle's huge table. He began to play his lute and sing in a soft voice. A lovely tune drifted through the musty air.

Groggle stared and stared. Then he closed his eyes and swayed back and forth as if he were thinking of a lullaby. He stayed that way, even when Sir Bryan put his lute down and cut the cords that bound the princess. Sir Bryan lifted the princess onto Charger's back.

Then suddenly Groggle's eyes opened, and he came at them, howling. Sir Bryan barely had time to grab his lute. Then he leaped on Charger's back behind Millicent.

> *Charger raced away,*
> *faster than sunlight,*
> *his mane flowing,*
> *his eyes glowing.*

They came to Bottomless River. Charger took one long leap over it to the other side.

But when clumsy Groggle tried to leap over, he fell into the river with a big splash. He sank all

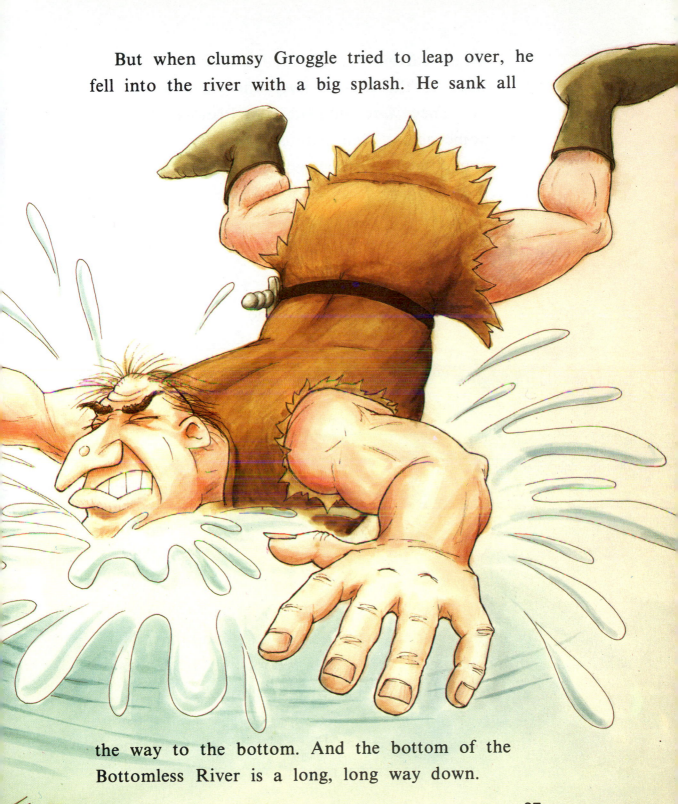

the way to the bottom. And the bottom of the Bottomless River is a long, long way down.

Charger carried Sir Bryan and Princess Millicent back to the palace. Everyone cheered and shouted. They were all glad that Princess Millicent was home again. And because the giant Groggle was gone, they even cheered Sir Bryan! Sir Bryan bowed and blushed, as only a brave and handsome knight can do.

King Edwin said, "Well, my boy, you have brought my daughter back to me. You have shown yourself to be a brave knight. I will reward you by giving you half my kingdom."

Sir Bryan had received his heart's desire when the people cheered for him, but he thanked the king for his generous reward.

Sir Bryan lived at the palace so he could rule his half of the kingdom. Soon he and Princess Millicent were married. And it is told that late in the evening the light, shimmery music of Sir Bryan's lute would float over the castle wall.

And in the moonlight
Charger would toss his head,
his mane flowing,
his eyes glowing.

Song Signals

Have you ever stopped to listen to the songs of the birds? Each kind of bird sings its own special song. If you listen carefully to the song, you may be able to identify the singing bird.

Most often birds sing to call their own families. Birds also signal to their mates by singing. Early in the spring, the birds' songs begin. When a mate is found, the pair fly off to make a home. Singing will protect their home by warning other birds to stay away.

Sometimes it seems that birds sing because they are happy. Their songs seem to praise God. The twittering "cheep, cheep, cheep" of a house sparrow adds cheer to bleak winter days. All year round the joyful "teakettle, teakettle" song of the Carolina wren can be heard.

The cries of the songbird are different from the songs they sing. The cries are used to signal the flock, warn others, or call for help.

When the catbird senses danger, it interrupts its song with a cat-like cry. The "mew, mew" warns the other birds to leave. Some brave birds aren't fooled by the catbird's signal, and they don't fly away. Then a fight often occurs to decide which bird will stay.

Have you ever thought about how sparrows all leave the tree at the same time? They are obeying a signal to leave. Birds use many cries to inform the flock. These cries are their signals.

The sharp cry of alarm may be given by any bird. Blue jays are an excellent alarm for the animals. The blue jays may warn forest animals of a hunter. Their sharp cries may also reveal a cat stalking a sparrow.

There are certain birds whose songs are really copies of other birds' songs. It seems as if they like to tease and mimic others. A blue jay may copy the songs of the catbird or wren. Then there are times when the shriek of "jay, jay, jay" is used to tease a cat.

The master mimic is the mockingbird. The Indians called this bird "four hundred tongues." It is able to make its songs sound like the songs of many other birds. The mockingbird also mimics other sounds. Its song may even sound like a flute or a whistle.

Listen carefully to the birds' songs. Can you tell what their signals mean?

46

Whistles

I want to learn to whistle,
I've always wanted to.
I fix my mouth to do it, but
The whistle won't come through.

I think perhaps it's stuck, and so
I try it once again.
Can people swallow whistles?
Where is my whistle then?

          Dorothy Aldis

The Locust's Song

Have you ever had trouble remembering something? In this adaptation of a traditional Indian tale, the coyote cannot remember a song, no matter how hard he tries!

Cast

Coyote	**Pigeons**
Locust	**Crow**
Gopher	**Fish**
Narrator	**Wind**

Narrator: Long ago there lived a coyote on the plains. At the edge of the plains was the forest. There, in a tall tree, lived a locust.

Each morning the coyote left his home and family to go hunting in the forest.

Each morning the singing locust sat on the branch of his tall tree.

One day while the coyote was hunting, he passed the tree and heard the locust's song.

Coyote: (looking up) Who is singing such wonderful music?

Locust: It is I who sings the locust's song.

Coyote: What a beautiful song!

Locust: What fine flattery! Tell me, is the song really as lovely as you say?

Coyote: Oh yes! Won't you teach it to me? My family would like to hear your song.

Locust: Very well. Listen carefully while I sing it again.

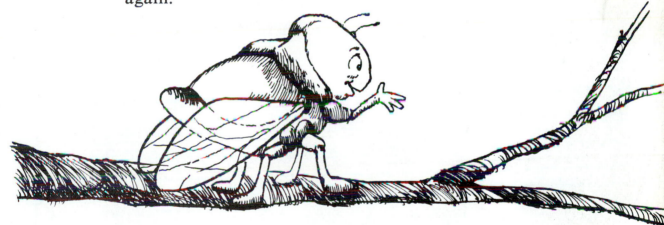

Narrator: The coyote listened. Then he tried to sing the song in his gruff voice.

Locust: Well, that sounds pretty good for the first try. Let's try again.

Coyote: I know it well enough now. I can almost hear it in my mind. I'll go and sing it to my family.

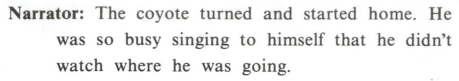

Narrator: The coyote turned and started home. He was so busy singing to himself that he didn't watch where he was going.

Crow: (cawing) Beware, beware!

Narrator: The coyote stepped into a gopher's hole, and down he went! Dust flew everywhere.

Coyote: Ka-choo! Ka-choo!

Gopher: Oh my, oh my!

Coyote: (angrily accusing) Gopher, you have made this path nothing but holes and dusty traps!

Gopher: (peering out of a hole in the path) You were not watching where you were going, Coyote.

Crow: Caw! Caw! You had your head in the air.

Gopher: Yes, what were you doing?

Coyote: (scrambling to his feet) I was singing. And you have made me forget my song!

Narrator: The coyote scratched his head. He thought and thought, but he couldn't remember the locust's song.

Coyote: (muttering) I suppose I'll have to go back to Locust. He will sing the song again for me.

Crow: Caw! Caw! I want to hear the song too.

Coyote: Well, come along, but be quiet!

Narrator: The coyote trotted back down the dusty path. The crow followed him, flapping his wings. At last Coyote reached the tree where the locust lived.

Coyote: (looking up) I was running home singing your song and Gopher dug a hole right in front of me and I fell down! I almost broke my leg and the song disappeared down the gopher's hole. Will you sing it just one more time?

Locust: Take care that you listen this time!

Narrator: The locust sang the song again. The coyote sat with his head tilted, listening to the song. Almost before the locust finished, the coyote jumped up.

Coyote: (boastfully) I've memorized the song.

Crow: Caw! Caw! Be sure, now. Be sure!

Coyote: I'll always remember it!

Narrator: The locust watched as the coyote started home again. The coyote sang the beautiful locust song as he trotted along the trail. As he finished the song, he tilted back his head and gave a long, loud howl.

Pigeons: (fluttering out of the tall grass along the trail) Coo! Coo! Don't startle us so!

Coyote: (falling backward) Oh, you silly birds. You have frightened the song right out of my head! I won't be able to take it home to my family.

Pigeons: Coo! What song?

Coyote: Why, the song I was singing, you silly birds.

Crow: Caw! The locust's song is gone!

Pigeons: (fluttering overhead) Coo! Why not learn our song? We'll teach you to sing like us.

Coyote: Thank you, but I wanted to take the locust's song back to my children. Now I'll have to go back and ask that locust to sing the song for me again.

Narrator: The coyote raced back to the tree where the locust lived. The crow flapped along above him.

Crow: Caw! I know the song!

Coyote: (panting) Quiet, Crow! I have to get to the tree before the locust is gone.

Coyote: (reaching the tree) Oh, friend, I'm glad to see you. As I was trotting home singing your song some silly pigeons flew up in front of me. I was so startled that the song flew away with them. Will you be kind enough to sing the song again?

Locust: (scolding) You are a careless coyote. However, I'll sing it for you one more time.

Narrator: Locust sang the song again. The coyote listened closely.

Coyote: Now I know the song as well as I know my name. Thank you, Locust!

Crow: Caw!

Narrator: The coyote left quickly for home, running as fast as he could run. He raced past the tall grass along the trail, singing as he ran.

Pigeons: Coo! Coo! We like your song too!

Narrator: The coyote nodded and kept on singing and running. He didn't want to forget the song this time! He ran down the path past the gopher's hole.

Gopher: (ducking his head) Watch out! You're kicking dust into my home!

Narrator: The coyote only ran faster. But once again he didn't watch where he was going.

Crow: (circling above the path) Caw! Look before you leap!

Narrator: As the coyote jumped over a rock, his foot slipped. He tumbled head over heels down the hillside.

Coyote: (Mumbling) Oh, my head! Oh, my head!

Narrator: The coyote sat up, rubbing his head. Above him the wind whistled and sang. It reminded him of the song.

Coyote: My song! My song is gone. Have you taken my song, Wind?

Wind: You were the one who was careless, Coyote. You lost your song. Next time don't be in such a hurry.

Coyote: (glumly) But I really did want to sing the song to my family. I wanted to get home before I lost it again.

Crow: Caw! Caw!

Coyote: Oh, be quiet, Crow!

Narrator: The coyote got up slowly and brushed himself off. He began to climb slowly back up the hill. At last he reached the locust's tree.

Locust: And what happened this time?

Coyote: The wind blew me down a hill. With a huff and a puff he blew my song away. Will you sing it just one more time?

Locust: (sternly) I have sung enough today.

Coyote: My family would like to hear your song. Won't you sing it for them?

Locust: (hesitating) Well, just for your little ones.

Narrator: The locust sang again and the coyote listened carefully. Above them the crow sat quietly, listening.

Locust: Now, that's all, Coyote!

Coyote: Thank you, I won't bother you again.

Narrator: The coyote trotted quickly away. It was now getting dark. The coyote could barely see the path in the darkness. He sang quietly to himself as he trotted along. At last he came to a stream. He tried to jump the stream, but in the darkness he misjudged how far he had to jump. Into the stream he fell.

Coyote: (Sputtering to the fish swimming around him) Out of my way, out of my way!

Fish: Watch out! You are getting our water muddy!

Coyote: Muddy water! That's the least of my troubles. I've forgotten that song again.

Narrator: Wet and tired, the coyote trotted back through the darkness to the locust's tree. But when he got there the locust was gone.

Coyote: Oh, my! Now what will I do? I have wasted the whole day, and I still don't have a song to sing for my little ones.

Crow: (still sitting in the tree where the locust had been) Caw!

Coyote: Oh, Crow! What will I do?

Crow: I can sing the song for you.

Coyote: What?

Narrator: The crow began to sing. Above him the roosting pigeons sang softly. Even the wind stopped blowing to listen. Then the wind began to sing too.

Pigeons: Coo! Coo!

Wind: O-O-O-O!

Narrator: The coyote listened, then began to sing with them. At last the song was finished.

Coyote: Thank you all! And thank you, Crow! Now will you go home with me and help me sing to my family?

Crow: Caw! Caw!

Narrator: The coyote and the crow started down the path, the coyote trotting along and the crow flapping above him. And as they went, they sang the locust's song. When they passed the gopher's hole, the gopher stuck out his head.

Gopher: (yawning) Why, that *is* a pretty song!

Narrator: He ducked back inside his hole, sleepily humming. The coyote trotted down the hill and splashed across the stream.

Fish: (blowing bubbles) We like your song too, Coyote.

Narrator: The fish began to sing quietly, blowing bubbles that drifted in the water. The coyote smiled. On the other side of the stream, he stopped to look up at the crow.

Crow: (softly) Caw! Caw!

Coyote: (softly) O-O-OOO!

The Amazing Mozart

On January 27, 1756, Leopold Mozart, the archbishop's musician, held his newborn son in his arms. As he hummed a lullaby and rocked Wolfgang to sleep, Herr Mozart must have wondered if his son would become a musician like himself. He never guessed that his little baby son would someday write over 600 pieces of music and be remembered all over the world.

Maria Anna Mozart finished practicing for her lesson. She put her music book away and left the clavier. Quickly, three-year-old Wolfgang climbed onto the bench. He began to play the notes he had heard.

Even when he was three, Wolfgang knew that some notes sounded nice together. He knew that others sounded bad. If he played notes that sounded bad, his eyes filled with tears. But when his melodies sounded nice, he was so excited that he would call his family to come and listen.

By the time Wolfgang was four, he could play many songs. Sometimes he would play an entire song from memory.

By the age of five, he was even writing some of his own music!

One day Wolfgang's papa brought some of his musician friends home. They found Wolfgang working hard over a piece of paper.

"I wrote this to play on the clavier," said Wolfgang, holding up the paper.

Papa smiled as he looked at the messy paper. Wolfgang had found it hard to write without dripping and spilling the ink. But he had no trouble with the music itself.

"See here," said Papa to his friends. "It is all written correctly. But it is very difficult. No one will be able to play it."

Wolfgang went to the clavier to play his music. But even though he could hear the music in his mind, it was so hard he could only play parts of it.

Wolfgang's gift for making music included more instruments than the clavier. He also liked to play the violin. When Wolfgang was six, he was given a violin as a present.

One evening, Papa and two friends sat down to practice. They were playing some new melodies for stringed instruments. Wolfgang asked if he could play the part of the second violin. But Papa shook his head. He had not taught Wolfgang to play the violin.

Papa's friends saw that the little boy was disappointed. One of the friends suggested that Wolfgang play the second part along with him.

"All right," Papa finally agreed. "You may play, Wolfgang. But you must play so softly that no one can hear you."

When the music was finished, tears were
running down Papa's cheeks. Wolfgang had played
the part perfectly.

Mozart's father knew that it was time to share his children's talents with people outside their hometown. He began to take his son and daughter to other cities. There, others could enjoy their music.

In almost every country the Mozarts visited, the children performed for the king and queen. Everyone enjoyed hearing them play. Wolfgang could play the clavier without a mistake, even when the keyboard was covered with a cloth!

In the city of Vienna, the children played for the Emperor and Empress. Maria Anna and Wolfgang pleased all those who listened. The Empress was even more charmed when small Wolfgang climbed on her lap and kissed her.

When Wolfgang was fourteen, he and his father visited the city of Rome. There they went to hear a special song. Only those who sang the marvelous song could see the music. Anyone who tried to copy the music would be punished.

Wolfgang listened carefully to the music. When he went home that night, he wrote the entire song from memory. The people of Rome were amazed that a young boy had been able to remember and write the song. They were so surprised that they forgot to punish him! Instead they went to his concerts to hear the talented boy play.

In Rome, Wolfgang was invited to become a member of a special music club. To become a member, he had to take a test. The test was very hard. It had never been given to anyone under twenty years old. But fourteen-year-old Wolfgang finished the test in much less time than anyone else had ever done! All the judges agreed that Wolfgang Mozart should become a member of their club.

Wolfgang kept writing music. He wrote and wrote, night and day. He wrote beautiful operas and other kinds of music.

It wasn't until after Mozart died that he became famous for his written music. Then people began to enjoy the music he had written, like "The Magic Flute."

Today we no longer remember him as Mozart, the amazing child, but as Mozart, the composer.

Alex, the Drummer Boy

This story is historical fiction. It takes place in January of 1781, when the colonies of America were fighting for their independence from England. The characters are real, and the story is based on a true event.

Patriot Spy

Alex McDonald's eyes sparkled as he stretched a piece of leather over his mother's clay water pot.

"I will m-m-make a drum fit for the g-g-great General Washington," he stuttered.

Alex put his homemade drum between his knees. He beat the drum with his hands, keeping time with the cold raindrops that fell all around the log cabin.

Alex could almost feel the thick wool drummer's coat on his back. He could almost hear a musket ball whizzing through the crisp, winter air.

"My drum would give orders to the soldiers," Alex thought. "We would drive the British from South Carolina. We would drive them toward General Washington."

Suddenly Alex jumped. A hand had touched his curly red hair.

"Lad, I did not mean to frighten you," said Alex's father as he sat down on the porch. "I need your help."

Alex smiled. "I w-w-will do anything to help you, Father."

"I have heard that the British general, Cornwallis, will be leaving here soon," Mr. McDonald said. "He has ordered us to bring food to his camp. I want you to take our old bull and some taters. While the soldiers get the money for the food, you can look around the camp."

Alex's knees shook and a hard lump settled in his stomach. "F-f-father, I c-c-cannot talk to s-s-strangers."

"You do not need to talk," said Mr. McDonald. "Just give them the food and keep your eyes and ears open. They will never guess that you are a patriot spy."

Mr. McDonald put his hand on his son's shoulder. "I have decided to join Daniel Morgan and the southern army," he said quietly. "I need this information."

Alex looked into his father's kind face. "I will do my b-b-best," he promised.

Later that afternoon, the rain slowed down to a drizzle. Alex took the sack of potatoes and drove the old bull to the British camp. He gave the bull and the potatoes to a gruff British soldier. The soldier wore a red coat and carried a shiny musket.

"Are you a friend of the rebels or of the king?" asked the soldier.

"I-I-I . . . ," Alex stuttered. How could he answer such a question?

Another soldier laughed and slapped the guard's back. "You should not frighten children," he said to his friend. He turned to Alex and added, "Come with me. I will pay you for these supplies."

Alex and the British soldier splashed through a muddy lane between rows of small tents. Inside the tents, hungry, red-coated men shivered. Some of the men slept on layers of wet, dirty straw. Others played games or cleaned their muskets.

The British soldier stopped before a larger tent. "Wait here," he said. "I will bring your payment."

He returned and dropped some coins into Alex's hand. "Now off with you," he said kindly and went back inside the tent.

Alex walked slowly through the camp, listening to the soldiers call to each other. He looked up as a rider galloped into camp. The rider called to Alex, "Here, boy. Hold my horse."

Quickly, Alex stepped across a mud puddle and took the horse's reins. He watched the man enter General Cornwallis' large tent. He heard the man say, "Sir, I have a letter from Lieutenant Colonel Tarleton."

Bloody Tarleton! Alex gasped. His father had told him about Colonel Tarleton. "The men call him 'Bloody' because he had our soldiers killed when they surrendered," Mr. McDonald had said. "He does not show mercy."

Alex leaned toward the tent flap. He heard about the British plans to destroy Daniel Morgan's army.

"I must warn Father," thought Alex. He handed the horse's reins to a passing soldier and walked away. At the edge of the camp, he began to run.

Patriot Messenger

The sun was just setting when Alex slammed the cabin door. "F-f-father," he gasped.

His father crossed the room and grabbed Alex's shoulders. "Slow down, lad, and tell me what you have heard."

The steady hum of the spinning wheel stopped. Alex's five sisters put down their knitting needles.

Alex took a deep breath. He told his father about the British's plans.

Mr. McDonald hung a long knife from his belt. He picked up his rifle, his powder horn, and his black felt hat.

"Alex and I must reach General Morgan's camp before the rivers overflow," he told his wife. "Alex must tell the general all that he has seen and heard. We must warn him that the British are coming."

Mrs. McDonald nodded and turned toward the big stone fireplace. "I will pack some bread and meat," she said. "Alex, climb up into the loft. Put on your new mittens and stockings, and get the thick quilt from your bed."

As he climbed into the loft, Alex wondered, "How will I ever answer General Morgan's questions?"

The days passed as Alex and his father rode almost sixty miles through bare forests and rushing creeks. Cold wind and rain followed them all the way to General Morgan's camp in the northeast corner of South Carolina.

A guard dressed in a fringed leather hunting shirt led Alex and his father to Daniel Morgan's tent. "The general does not feel well," said the guard. "You must not stay too long."

Alex waited outside as his father stepped into the general's tent. A few minutes later Mr. McDonald called Alex. Alex's heart pounded like a hammer as he entered the tent.

General Morgan groaned as he stood up and greeted Alex.

"The cold rains make my back and joints ache," explained the general. He pointed to a canvas folding chair. "Sit down, sir," he said to Mr. McDonald.

Mr. McDonald leaned his rifle against a tent pole and sat down. "This is my son, Alexander. He has some information for you."

Daniel Morgan stretched and looked at Alex, "Your father tells me you have been in the camp of that old fox, Cornwallis. Is this true?"

Alex gulped and rubbed his sweaty palms against his shirt. "I-I-I w-w-went to . . . ," he began, but could not finish. He hung his head in shame.

His father spoke quietly. "Alex stutters, sir."

The general lifted Alex up and set him on a rough wooden table.

"Twenty years ago I fought with the British against the French and Indians. One day a musket ball went into the back of my neck and through my mouth. My wound healed but it left behind this scar on my cheek," said Daniel Morgan. "For a long time I talked as if I had leather in my mouth. I had to speak slowly and carefully. You should do the same."

The general smiled at Alex. "Now try once more, my boy," he urged. "Tell me your story."

Alex took a deep breath and said, "Yes, sir, I took some taters and the old b-b-bull down to the British c-c-camp. Father told me not to f-f-forget anything I heard."

General Morgan opened a pouch which hung from his belt and pulled out a coin. "Tell me all you know," he said, handing the coin to Alex.

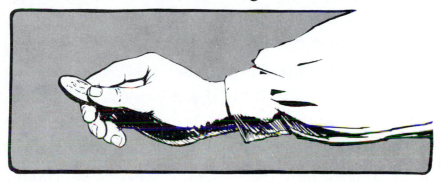

"No, thank you," Alex said, handing the coin back to the general. "I was near Lord C-C-Cornwallis's tent when a rider came into camp. The m-m-man was from Bloody Tarleton. He brought plans to d-d-destroy you. Lord C-C-Cornwallis ordered Colonel T-T-Tarleton to take a thousand men and f-f-fight you wherever you could be found. Lord C-C-Cornwallis will f-f-follow in a few days."

Once again General Morgan held out the gold coin. "My dear boy! You have given us information of great value. Now will you accept the gold piece?"

Alex shook his head.

"May I give you something else?" asked the general.

Alex blushed and said very softly, "I w-w-wish to be a drummer b-b-boy."

The general rubbed his chin. "When an officer gives a command, the drummer must beat out the proper signal," he said. "If a drummer gives the wrong signal, men could be killed or wounded. The battle could be lost."

"I would l-l-learn the signals," said Alex.

"Would you learn from the other drummers?" asked Daniel Morgan. "Would you obey the officers in all things?"

Alex looked into the general's eyes. "Yes, sir. I would do my b-b-best."

The general still was not sure. "My boy, the drummers are in great danger during each battle," he said. "The enemy will often shoot them because the drummers pass along the officers' orders to the men."

Alex jumped off the table. "Sir, I want to help d-d-drive the British from our land!"

"If your father agrees, you may stay," said General Morgan.

Mr. McDonald picked up his rifle and stood at the tent flap. "You have a new drummer boy, General," he said, smiling.

Drummer Boy

General Morgan introduced Alex to Jake Wilson, one of the older drummer boys. "Take care of him, Jake," said the general before he left. "Show him all the drum signals that he must know.

Jake smiled and handed Alex his drum. "This is our special practice time," he said to Alex. "The soldiers know that all the drummers are practicing their signals. They will ignore us."

"May I practice by m-m-myself?" asked Alex.

Jake shook his head. "No. You must never beat the drum for fun. The soldiers would think that you were giving them a signal. Now, listen well," Jake added. "This is your first signal."

Alex listened carefully to each signal. He learned to strike his drum with steady strokes.

The days passed. Alex learned to beat short strokes, long strokes, and quick, fast drumrolls.

One week later, on January 16, Alex shivered as he marched beside the soldiers in their blue coats. He carried a red drum which had been painted to match his heavy coat.

Alex listened carefully. His friend Jake was beating his drum. Jake's drum said, "Front to halt!" Alex passed the signal to the other drummers, and the whole army stopped.

General Morgan pointed toward the Cowpens where thousands of cattle grazed each spring.

"We'll stand and fight here," he said. "On this ground I will defeat the British or lay my bones."

Alex and the other drummers beat the camp signals. Some of the soldiers gathered wood, made campfires, and dried their wet clothes. Some passed out food and gunpowder from the wagons. Others fed and watered their horses. The scouts guarded the camp.

After supper, Alex visited his father's campfire. "Will we h-h-have enough men to f-f-fight?" he asked.

"Riflemen are coming from miles around," said Alex's father as he cleaned his rifle. "We will give Bloody Tarleton a good fight."

The night passed slowly. Daniel Morgan walked from campfire to campfire. He joked with the men and explained his battle plan.

"Keep in good spirits and the day will be ours," he said.

Later that night, Alex saw the general limp into the nearby woods. He punched Jake. "Where is the g-g-general going?" he whispered.

Jake rolled over. "General Morgan always prays for our protection during a battle," he said. "Go to sleep."

Alex felt much safer. He was sure that God would protect their army.

Early the next morning the scouts rode into camp. "Tarleton is only five miles away!" they shouted.

General Morgan yelled, "Boys, get up!"

Alex ran to his drum. He hung it around his neck. Then he and the other drummers beat the signals on their drums.

"Prepare to march!"

"Form companies!"

The soldiers and riflemen quickly threw their belongings into the wagons. As the men lined up, the wagons jolted into the woods behind the field.

Alex and the other drummers gave the marching signal. The men marched onto the grassy, sloping field. They formed three long battle lines.

General Morgan rode along the two front lines.

"Wait until the enemy is close," he said. "Fire two shots and then retreat to the second line."

Alex's father waited in the second line. He lay in the high grass with the rest of the riflemen.

The soldiers in Alex's company stood in the third line, near the top of the grassy slope.

"I have confidence in your skill and courage," said General Morgan to the men in Alex's company. "Stand firm and obey your officer, Colonel Howard. Soldiers on horses are waiting behind the hill to surprise the British."

Alex watched as one thousand British soldiers lined up behind two cannons. He saw British horsemen in green uniforms and soldiers in bright red coats. He also saw Scottish soldiers who wore kilts and played bagpipes.

While Alex watched, fifty British horsemen galloped toward the front line. Morgan's riflemen fired and black smoke covered the field. When the smoke cleared, fifteen of the horsemen had fallen from their saddles. The others were riding back to the trees.

The riflemen turned and ran to the second line. Behind them, cannons roared, and the British soldiers marched forward.

Alex saw his father in the second line. He watched his father take aim, fire, and retreat up the slope.

Suddenly Alex gasped. His father had fallen! "Father, get up!" Alex yelled.

"Drummer, order the men to fire!" shouted Colonel Howard.

Alex wanted to run to his father, but he had promised to obey the officers. For thirty minutes Alex beat his drum, trying not to look at the place where his father lay.

"Make ready!" "Fire!" "Cease firing!"

"Make ready!" "Fire!" "Cease firing!"

Again and again Alex beat his drum until his arms were so tired they felt as wooden as his drumsticks.

Alex looked up as Colonel Howard stopped beside him. "Tell your men to turn and face the soldiers on their right side," the colonel said.

Again Alex lifted his drumsticks. There was no time to think. He quickly beat the signal.

"We must win," he thought. "We must win!"

Alex watched as the men in his company turned and retreated. Soon the whole line was retreating.

"I gave the wrong s-s-signal," Alex cried to the angry Colonel Howard.

General Morgan rode over to Alex and Colonel Howard. "Why are your men retreating?" he asked. "Are they beaten?"

"Do men who march like that look like they are beaten?" asked Colonel Howard.

General Morgan watched the men and quickly decided on a new plan. "I will tell them when to face about and fire," he said to Colonel Howard.

Alex looked down the long line. Where was Jake? "I cannot g-g-give the signal," he said to the men.

"Jake has been wounded," General Morgan said. "I am depending on you."

Alex had no choice. "Dear God, please h-h-help me," he prayed.

When the soldiers had reached a certain spot, General Morgan said to Alex, "Beat the signal to face about! Give them one fire, and the day is ours!"

Quickly Alex beat three single strokes, then a short and a long stroke. He watched as the soldiers turned, knelt, and fired.

At the same moment, American horsemen and riflemen surrounded the British. Colonel Tarleton and two hundred British horsemen broke through the lines and galloped away. Many of the British soldiers threw down their guns, knelt, and begged for mercy.

Alex ran down the hill, past fallen men. He knelt by his father. "Father, are y-y-you all right?" he asked.

Mr. McDonald raised his head. "A musket ball hit my leg," he said. "Would you go to the wagons and get my horse? I will ride to our campsite and get my leg bandaged."

General Morgan stopped beside them. "I'll give Alex a ride back to the camp, Mr. McDonald. Then he can bring your horse back."

He held out his hand to Alex, "We have won the day, drummer boy!"

SPECIAL DEEDS

SPACE WALK

For months Major White and Commander McDivitt had trained every day. They had learned to float in space. They had learned to use an air gun to move in space. Now their training would be put to use. Today Major White would be the first American to walk in space!

On June 3, 1965, *Gemini IV* stood on the launching pad. At 4:10 in the morning, Major White and Commander McDivitt woke up. Liftoff time would be 9:00.

As the two men prepared for the flight, scientists moved quickly about the launching pad. The huge rocket was checked and re-checked.

At last Major White and Commander McDivitt were ready. An elevator carried them up to start their journey. The elevator stopped at the hatch of the huge space ship. The astronauts climbed in and buckled up their safety harnesses.

The big tower beside the rocket lowered. But it stopped before it reached the ground. Then it raised up to the hatch again. Something was wrong!

The scientists went to work. After a careful search they found a connector that had been put in wrong. As quickly as possible a workman repaired it.

Mission Control set a new liftoff time—10:16 A.M.

The astronauts were ready. The rocket engines hummed—10-9-8-7-6-5-4-3-2-1-blast off!

Gemini IV lifted into the air with a thunderous roar.

Inside the spacecraft Major White and Commander McDivitt couldn't hear the rumbling blast of the engines, but they felt the rocket soar into the sky. *Gemini IV* climbed out of sight of the earthbound spectators and started to circle the earth.

The first stage of the rocket fell off. All the fuel inside had been burned up as they blasted off. Later the second stage fell off when its fuel was gone.

Commander McDivitt started reading a check list. He marked off each thing that had to be done before Major White's space walk.

Major White began putting his air gun together. He tied the air gun to his arm and hooked an oxygen tube to his suit. Now he was ready for the space walk!

Back on earth Mission Control told him to go ahead.

Major White tried to unlatch the hatchway. It wouldn't budge. He tugged until it opened a crack. Then he heaved and pushed until it slid back.

Slowly he climbed out into space. He floated beside the hatchway for a moment.

Then he pointed the air gun downward. He pulled the trigger. The thrust of air from the gun pushed him up the side of the spacecraft. As Major White walked across the spacecraft, the Commander heard the thump, thump of his spaceboots. Major White rolled down the other side of the spacecraft. He drifted down to Commander McDivitt's window. The Commander snapped his picture.

Then Major White rolled over and faced earth. His voice came over the radio, describing what he saw. The beautiful world shone below him. "I can sit out here and see the whole California coast," he said.

He rolled over two more times before his air gun ran out of fuel.

"Back in, come on," the Commander said.

"I'm not coming in," Major White laughed.

"Come on, get back in here before it gets dark," the Commander said.

"Okay, I'm going to come in the house," said Major White. He glanced at planet earth once more. "This is the saddest moment of my life," he said as he drifted through the hatchway.

Major White tugged at the hatch as he slipped into his chair. It wouldn't lock. He tugged harder. As he pulled he floated out of his seat. Commander McDivitt grabbed his legs and dragged him back. The lock clicked into place.

Major White's walk in space had lasted twenty-one minutes.

They orbited the earth sixty-two times. Then the Commander fired the retrorockets. The two astronauts heard the bang, bang, bang, bang as the rockets exploded into action. *Gemini IV* turned back to earth. Their journey into space was over. The big space ship plunged back to the earth.

In just a few minutes the rocket splashed into the sea.

A helicopter spotted Major White and Commander McDivitt. It picked them up and took them to the aircraft carrier *Wasp*.

The space walk had been a success.

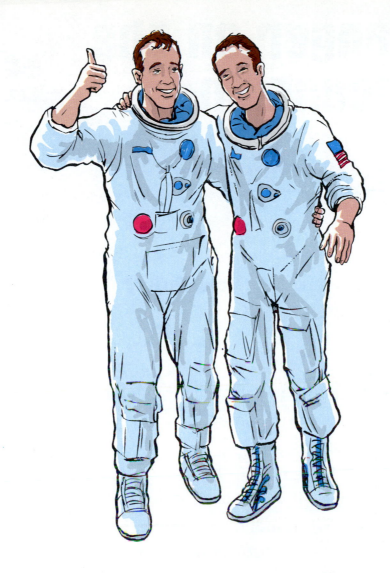

Later the Commander stopped to talk to a newsman. "I did not see God looking into my space cabin window," he said, "as I did not see God looking into my car's windshield on earth. But I could recognize His work in the stars as well as when walking among the flowers in a garden. If you can be with God on earth, you can be with God in space."

Danger on the Mountain

A New Puppy

Hansel stamped his feet to shake the snow off his boots. Then he carried his armload of firewood into the kitchen. Grandmother shivered as he dropped the firewood into the wooden box near the stove.

"It's getting colder, Hansel," she said, smiling at him. "Make sure the back door is closed tightly."

"When is Grandfather coming home?" asked Hansel as he pushed hard on the door.

Grandmother glanced at the old clock above the table. "He's late now," she said. "He stopped at Pastor's house to drop off a load of firewood. They probably got to talking, as always. He'll be along soon."

Hansel rubbed a circle on the windowpane and peered out. "Here he comes now! He has a big basket with him."

Hansel hurried to open the door. Grandfather came in, still carrying the big basket.

"What's that, Grandfather?" Hansel asked.

Grandfather's eyes twinkled. "Oh, just a little something for you," he teased.

Grandmother wiped her hands and came to look over their shoulders as Grandfather put the basket on the floor.

The covering on the basket quivered, and a soft nose appeared under the edge of the rough cloth. Then the covering slid and a puppy sat up, one edge of the cloth draped over one eye.

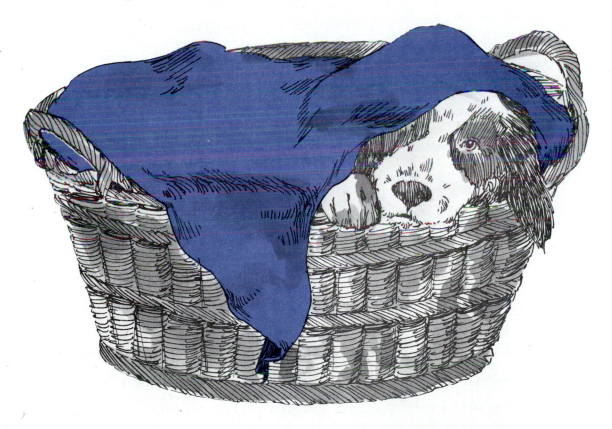

"A puppy! For me?" Hansel exclaimed, gathering the puppy up in his arms.

"That's what Pastor said, just for you." Grandfather smiled. "He's a Saint Bernard. His mother died when he was born, so we will have to take special care of him. What do you think of him?"

"He's terrific!" Hansel grinned happily as the puppy wiggled and licked his face.

"And just what are you going to call this fine puppy?" asked Grandmother. "He should have a special name."

Hansel held the puppy still enough to gaze into his brown eyes. "You are an orphan just like me," he said. "I will call you Orphan."

Grandmother gave Hansel a hug. "That's a fine name," she said. "Now I'll find him a warm corner while you go get ready for supper."

Orphan

As the months went by, Orphan grew bigger and bigger. Soon, instead of carrying Orphan, Hansel found that he could ride on Orphan's back. Through the spring and the summer, Hansel and Orphan played together. Hansel grew strong and brown in the sun. Orphan just grew!

Hansel's friend Markus liked Orphan too. The boys and Orphan spent many long summer hours racing through the woods and along the green slopes of the mountain.

"I declare," said Grandmother as she watched them one day. "I don't think those three have left one stone unturned on this mountain!"

Grandfather laughed. "They're just boys," he said. Then he added, "It's good to know the land. In the winter the mountain can be dangerous. It is good for them to know what lies hidden under a blanket of winter snow."

Grandmother nodded. "I pray the Lord will take care of them when winter comes. I always hate to have them ski down the mountain to school."

"That is the way it has always been, Mother," said Grandfather. "We must teach them what we can and trust the Lord to take care of them."

As autumn came closer, Grandfather went with Hansel and Markus more often. He taught them where the safe ski trails would be when snow blanketed the land. He showed them dangerous spots where snowdrifts would pile up over their heads. And everywhere they went, Orphan followed.

Soon September came and it was time to go to school in the valley. Every day Hansel walked down the slope to Markus's house. Together they walked the rest of the way down the mountain to school. In the afternoons Orphan met Hansel at Markus's house. He and Hansel would race the rest of the way home.

The leaves changed color and fell from the trees. The boys waxed their skis and began exercising to make their ankles stronger. Orphan sniffed the strange boards tied to the boys' feet.

"Oh, Orphan," cried Hansel. "Watch out!"

For the second time Orphan had run in front of him as he practiced walking on the skis.

Markus laughed as Hansel landed in a heap on top of Orphan.

But soon Orphan got used to the strange boards the boys called skis. And at last the day came that the boys had been waiting for.

Hansel came running in from the barn. "It's snowing! It's snowing!" he called.

Grandfather looked up from his leatherwork. "Yes," he said. "There will be lots of snow on the ground by morning."

"Enough to ski to school?" asked Hansel eagerly.

"Enough to ski to school," replied Grandfather, smiling.

Danger

The next morning Hansel put on his coat, hat, and mittens. He strapped his schoolpack onto his back. Grandmother went to the door to watch Hansel buckle on his skis.

Orphan was too busy with the funny white stuff on the ground to pay attention to the skis this morning. He jumped and rolled in the snow. Then he tried to run, plowing through the snow and sending sprays of powdery snow over everyone.

"Be careful, Orphan." Hansel laughed. "I don't want to have to dig you out! I must be at school before eight."

Grandmother and Grandfather waved goodbye as Hansel skied down the slope to Markus's house. Orphan plowed through the snow after him.

Grandfather looked down at Grandmother's worried face. "Now, Mother," he said, "Let's just pray and leave it with the Lord."

Each morning the boys skied to school. Each afternoon Orphan met them at Markus's house. The days went by quickly.

Then one morning Grandfather looked at the sky and shook his head. "It just doesn't look right today, Hansel," he said.

"Why not, Grandfather?" asked Hansel, looking at the sky.

"Bad weather is coming," replied Grandfather. "Be careful today, son."

"I will, Grandfather," promised Hansel. Before he left the house, he and his grandparents took more time than usual in prayer. Then Hansel left for school. Orphan followed but came back later whining softly. Then he lay down outside, facing the ski trail.

By noon, the sky had turned a flat gray. The teacher dismissed school early. Hansel and Markus strapped their skis to their backs and hurried up the trail, keeping watchful eyes on the darkening sky.

Suddenly Markus called, "Wait, Hansel!"

Hansel turned back. Markus was down on one knee, holding his ankle. Hansel stopped beside him just as snow began to fall. "I've twisted my ankle," said Markus.

"Did you break it?" Hansel asked, kneeling beside Markus.

"No," Markus replied as he stood up slowly. "But I can't walk. What will we do?"

Rescue

Snow began falling faster, swirling around Markus and Hansel. The icy flakes stung their faces.

Markus hobbled on his ankle. "Go on, Hansel. You can get help."

"No, I won't leave you," Hansel replied. "They'll send help when we don't get home on time."

"But we left school early today," said Markus. "They won't know! They'll think we are safe in school."

By now they could no longer see more than a few feet in front of them.

"We must remember what Grandfather taught us," said Hansel. "We must find shelter through the storm."

The boys made their way slowly to the shelter of some overhanging rocks that Grandfather had pointed out so long ago. They huddled close together to keep warm.

They talked for awhile about different things, then sat watching the white sheet of snow.

"We'll be all right, Markus," said Hansel. "I know we will."

"How can you know?" Markus asked. "We might never be found!"

"Because we prayed about this just this morning," said Hansel. "And I know the Lord will answer our prayer."

Markus nodded. "Yes, I know the Lord answers prayer."

For a moment the boys didn't speak. They stared out into the whirling snow. Then without looking at Hansel, Markus spoke quietly, "But I'm still afraid."

"So am I," Hansel replied slowly. "Let's pray and ask the Lord to give us courage and to help Grandfather to find us quickly."

Both boys bowed their heads and began to pray.

The snow piled higher and higher on the mountain.

At the house Orphan raced back and forth, whining and scratching at the door.

Grandfather nodded. "I know how you feel, Orphan. And I know what we both can do about it."

Grandmother got warm clothing for him while he went to the porch to get rope and snowshoes.

Grandfather tied the rope carefully to Orphan and put on the snowshoes. Then he and Orphan walked out into the white storm.

The icy wind whipped at them, but Grandfather bent his head and held on to the rope. Orphan plowed through the snow, moving slowly down the trail.

Then as they passed the barn, the swirling snow lessened, and Grandfather could see ahead of him. He felt a tug on the rope as Orphan, too, moved ahead more freely. Grandfather strained to see farther along the trail in front of him, but all he could see were the outlines of the tall evergreens that bordered the trail. He and Orphan moved slowly along the trees. As they neared the overhanging rocks, Orphan stopped and raised his head. He barked and swung off the trail.

"Good boy," said Grandfather, moving with the dog. They found the boys huddled under the rocks.

"Orphan!" Hansel sat up as Orphan licked his face. "You made it, Grandfather!"

Grandfather looked at Markus's ankle, then lifted him onto his back.

"We are all right, Hansel," Markus said. "Just like you said we would be. The Lord helped your grandfather to find us."

"And He gave us courage when we were afraid," said Hansel.

Ahead of them Orphan gave a quick bark. "Come on," he seemed to say, "Come on!"

New Year in a New Land

The Old Ways

Sonya walked quickly past the doors of the other apartments.

"Hello," called Mrs. Tallman cheerfully.

Sonya glanced up at her neighbor standing in her doorway. "Hello," she replied shyly. She edged toward the stairs that led to her own apartment.

"How do you like living in America?" Mrs. Tallman asked.

"I like . . . fine," Sonya said and put her foot on the first step.

Mrs. Tallman smiled at her, but Sonya turned and darted up the stairs.

Outside her apartment she paused to touch the little brass mezuzah box. A tiny scroll had been folded inside it. Sonya had never seen it, but she knew the commandments written on it by heart. She remembered the day Papa had unhooked it from their apartment door in Russia. She thought about their dangerous journey to America. Here they didn't have to be afraid anymore. But Sonya always was.

"Who is there?" Rachel called. "Sonya, is that you at the door?"

Sonya slipped inside and closed the door. Jacob sat at the table with his schoolbooks spread out in front of him.

"Boo!" Rachel said, jumping from behind the door.

Sonya giggled and gave Rachel a hug.

"Please clear off the table for dinner, Jacob," Mama said.

Quickly Sonya and Rachel set the plates on the table. Then Sonya heard Papa's heavy footsteps on the stairs.

As he opened the door the girls pounced on him. He swept them off their feet with a big bear hug.

But at supper Papa sat quietly, listening to everyone else talk. When Mama started to clear the table, he stopped her.

"We must talk," he said. "Children, we did not have much in Russia. Many times we were hungry." Papa looked at each of them. "Now I have a good job here in America. But I do not get paid for several weeks. We must be careful with the money we brought with us."

He stopped to look at Sonya's face. "This Sabbath day is the Jewish New Year. We have no money to buy fruit and honey to celebrate. This year we will just have each other."

"That is enough," Mama said.

Rachel and Jacob nodded, but as hard as she tried, Sonya could not keep back a tear. It slid down her cheek before she could hide it.

"Now, Sonya," Papa said. "Next year we will have a great feast."

"Oh, Papa, I am glad we have each other," Sonya said, putting her arms around his neck. "But I miss our friends and the old ways in Russia."

Mama patted Sonya's arm. "She is young, Papa," Mama said. "Now, whose turn is it to help with the dishes?"

"Mine, Mama," Rachel replied.

Papa talked to Sonya as Mama and Rachel cleared the dishes from the table. At last Sonya tiptoed off to bed.

Rachel sat down across from Jacob as he spread out his books again.

"I wish we could have a New Year's feast for Sonya," she said.

Jacob put his pencil down. "The Tallmans have always been very friendly. We could ask Mr. Tallman if he needs help in his market. Maybe we could get enough for a little New Year's feast."

"Jacob, what a good idea!" Rachel said excitedly. "Let's ask Papa if we may!"

Sonya's New Year's Feast

Jacob swept the storeroom while Rachel dusted the shelves. Then they put cans on the shelves.

"Well, I see the Lord has sent me some hard workers," Mr. Tallman said as they put away their aprons. "You may work every afternoon for one hour."

He smiled as Jacob and Rachel grinned at each other. "Payday is next Tuesday," he said as he turned away. He did not see them look at each other in dismay. Tuesday would be after the New Year! Sonya would not have her feast after all!

Just then the bell on the door jingled and Sonya peeked in.

"Rachel," she whispered in Russian, "Mama wants you to bring home a box of salt."

"Hello," said Mr. Tallman. "Who is this?"

Rachel pulled Sonya in the door. "This is Sonya, Mr. Tallman. She is our sister."

"Oh, yes, my wife has told me about young Sonya," Mr. Tallman said. He smiled at Sonya's surprised look. He picked up a shiny red apple and placed it in her hand. "Go ahead and eat it," he said.

Sonya looked at the apple. Then she looked up at Mr. Tallman. "If you please, may I take it home?"

Puzzled, Mr. Tallman asked, "Why not eat it here?"

"Sonya is thinking about the New Year's feast, Mr. Tallman," said Rachel. "That is why we wanted to get jobs. So we could buy apples and honey for the feast."

Mr. Tallman leaned against the counter, thinking. "And Tuesday payday is after the New Year," he said.

Slowly, Jacob and Rachel nodded.

"Well," Mr. Tallman smiled. "Whose store is this? Mine! I can have payday any time I want, can't I?"

Jacob began to smile. Rachel and Sonya watched Mr. Tallman with wide eyes.

"Now," Mr. Tallman said, looking at Sonya.
"You are Sonya Kuril, and you have a sister,
Rachel, and a brother, Jacob." He pretended to
count on his fingers. "And a mother and a father,
that makes five."

Mr. Tallman picked up his note pad. "This will do," he said. He wrote on the pad for a minute. Sonya looked at Jacob. He raised his eyebrows and shrugged his shoulders.

Then Mr. Tallman ripped off the page and handed it to Sonya. "Can you read English?" he asked.

"Yes, sir," Sonya replied.

"Read it out loud," Jacob said, trying to peek over her arm.

"Give to Sonya five apples, a bunch of grapes, and a bag of oranges . . ." Sonya said. She stopped in amazement.

"Keep going," Rachel poked her.

"And a jar of honey!" Sonya exclaimed.

"For the New Year," Mr. Tallman explained. "Rachel and Jacob are such good workers that I am giving them part of their money ahead of time. What is left I will give them on the regular payday, Tuesday."

"Why would you do this?" asked Jacob. "You are not Jewish."

"No," replied Mr. Tallman, "but I am a Christian. Jesus teaches that we should give of what we have to the stranger in our midst. And you are strangers to our land, aren't you?" he added with a twinkle in his eye.

Jacob nodded thoughtfully. "I have heard Papa say that you believe Jesus is the Messiah. I would like to hear more about Him. I think Papa would too."

"I will talk to your father," said Mr. Tallman. "But for now, we need to fill Sonya's order."

He picked up a bag and began filling it with fruit. Then he put a jar of honey on top.

Even Sonya waved happily as they left the market. The three sang as they walked up the stairs to their apartment.

Sonya stopped in front of the door to touch the mezuzah box. "I think I like this new land," she said. "I think it will be a good year, after all!"

PECOS BILL

(a tall tale)

A tale is a story that someone has invented to make folks laugh or cry or think. Some tales, at least the specially good ones, do more than that. They make you slap your knee and guffaw, or roll on the floor and howl. Those stories are the tall tales. The tales that just can't be true, but sure as a shooting star you wish they really could come true somewhere, somehow.

Pecos Looks for a Horse

Away out West where the coyotes howl, there lived the rootinest, tootinest cowboy of all. His name was Pecos Bill.

Now Pecos Bill wasn't like just any cowboy that you see every day. Some said that he had grown up on the desert with a pack of coyotes. And sometimes the other cowboys almost believed the old tale. Why, Pecos could outhowl the biggest wolf, outfight the meanest grizzly bear, and outrun the fastest horse.

Before any other cowboy could get his foot in the stirrup, Pecos had run almost into the next county. But still, the cowboys thought that Pecos looked strange running around the range on foot.

"Bill," said Gun Smith, "no self-respecting cowboy should be seen running around the range without a horse. It just doesn't seem right."

Pecos scratched his neck with a spiny cactus leaf. "You know, Smith," he replied, "maybe you are right. Maybe I should get a horse. But one thing is certain. I will not ride one of those poky horses you keep in your stables. I must find one that is as swift as lightning and as terrifying as thunder."

And without so much as a by-your-leave or a wish-me-well, Pecos Bill vanished over the hillside. Gun Smith stood in Pecos's dust, scratching his head and wondering again how Bill ever learned to run so fast. Maybe the coyotes really had taught him!

Pecos Bill ran on into the next state. In every town he stopped to ask if anyone had heard of a horse that was faster than a lightning bolt.

"Well, sir," drawled one old rancher, "I've heard tell of a big horse that runs so fast that no one can tell if he's white or gold."

The other townsfolk shook their heads. "You'll never catch that horse, though," they warned. "He's never been roped and never been ridden."

Pecos just laughed. But in every town he heard the same story.

"They call him Widow Maker," said the barber, leaning over to shave Pecos's chin. "Any man who wants to ride Widow Maker might as well tell his family good-bye!"

Pecos chuckled as he rubbed his chin. "Widow Maker?" he said and laughed outright.

He thanked the barber and raced away. In the next two days he ran from the plains of Montana to the border of Mexico. He ran until his feet ached from running. But never, never did he catch sight of Widow Maker.

Well, Pecos Bill finally gave up looking for that horse. He tried riding just about everything else he could think of.

He saddled a lightning bolt and rode it. It was fast enough, but it had only one direction—down!

He saddled a tornado and rode it across the plains. It twisted this way and that. When Pecos got off, his head was spinning around and around.

"No, nothing will do except a horse," he said to himself. Pecos sat down under a cactus to rest. He watched an ant crawl into a hole in the sand, then struggle up the other side.

"That looks like a hoofprint," Pecos said sleepily. "But it can't be. I've never seen a hoofprint as big as a dinner plate."

Then he sat up and looked again. "As big as a dinner plate!" His shout echoed in the canyon. "That must have been made by Widow Maker!"

Widow Maker

Pecos jumped up and ran, following the trail Widow Maker had left. From time to time the prints joined smaller hoofprints.

"There must be nine hundred eighty-seven mares in this herd," Pecos thought. "And Widow Maker looks like the leader."

After a few days, he saw the horses grazing at the bottom of a canyon. The nine hundred eighty-seven mares tossed their manes and whinnied. But Pecos had no time for them. He watched the big mustang standing in the middle of the herd. Widow Maker was twice as tall as the mares. He was golden all over except for a white mane, a white tail, and white legs.

"That is the horse I will have," Pecos declared. He tied his rope into a lariat and lassoed Widow Maker.

With one snort and a powerful jump, Widow Maker raced away. The rope snapped like a banjo string.

Pecos Bill grinned. "That horse has spirit," he said. "But so have I!"

And off Pecos raced after Widow Maker. All that afternoon, all that night, and all the next day Pecos raced the mustang. Widow Maker tossed his mane and whinnied, almost if he were laughing at the man who dared to try to catch him.

But Pecos did not give up. On the third day of the long chase, Widow Maker jumped over a little mountain and caught his hoof on a rock. It was only a split second before he was up and running again. But that split second was all Pecos Bill needed. With one leap, he landed on Widow Maker's back.

"Ya-hoo!" Pecos yelled.

Widow Maker kicked hard enough to send any other man to the top of Pike's Peak. But Pecos hung on tighter.

Widow Maker reared up so high that any other man would have hit the ground hard enough to make another Grand Canyon in the West. But Pecos just hung on tighter.

Widow Maker flipped a double flip and rolled over in the dirt so many times that any other man would have been crushed flat. But Pecos Bill hung on.

At last Widow Maker stood panting with his head hung low, as if to say, "You win, cowboy. I've met my match."

Pecos patted Widow Maker on the neck. "Widow Maker," he said. "You're the only creature I've ever met that gave me a good fight. I admire you for that. So I'm going to give you a choice."

Pecos got off Widow Maker's back and sat down on a rock. He broke open a cactus for himself and one for Widow Maker. They both drank thirstily. "You see, Widow Maker," Pecos said, "we have a big job to do. This wild West has to be tamed. I might be able to do it all by myself, but it would take me a long time. You can help me do it faster."

Widow Maker tossed his mane and stomped his hoof.

"Now, you could go back to your free and easy life," said Pecos Bill. "Or you could help me finish this big job. It's up to you."

Widow Maker trotted back and forth. Pecos Bill waited, not saying anything else. After a while, Widow Maker trotted back up to Pecos. He pushed his muzzle into Pecos Bill's hand.

The cowboys stared in amazement that evening as they saw who rode into camp. Pecos Bill and Widow Maker! What a team!

From that time on, Pecos Bill and Widow Maker set out to tame the West. And tame it they did—from the Mississippi River to the California coast. But Widow Maker never let anyone ride him except Pecos Bill. Anyone else who tried took a quick trip to Pike's Peak.

And, believe me, it's a long walk home from Pike's Peak!

Jim

There never was a nicer boy
Than Mrs. Jackson's Jim.
The sun should drop its greatest gold
On him.

Because, when Mother-dear was sick,
He brought her cocoa in.
And brought her broth, and brought her
    bread.
And brought her medicine.

And, tipping, tidied up her room.
And would not let her see
He missed his game of baseball
Terribly.

Gwyndolyn Brooks

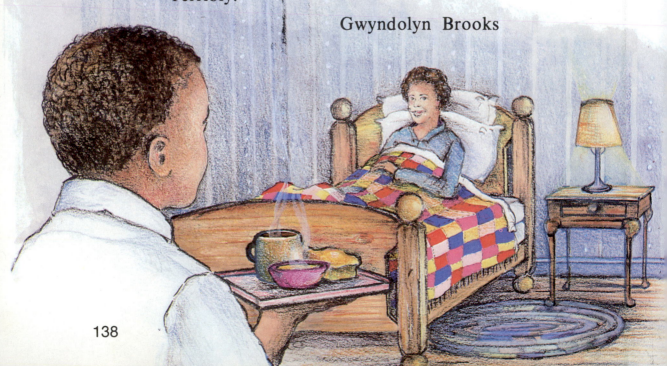

138

The Penguin Who Wanted to Fly

Leonard the penguin excelled in sliding, splashing, swimming, and especially quacking. Lennie and his family and friends lived on a giant iceberg in Antarctica, which is a very fun place to live. Winter vacation was the best time of the year too. This probably would have been Lennie's best winter ever, if only something hadn't happened—which is what this story is about.

"Hey, Penelope, watch me!" hollered Pete Penguin. "Wheee!" he cried as he slid down the icy slope backwards and splashed into the water. Just arriving, Lennie heard squeals of delight from all the neighborhood girl penguins as his friend Pete climbed out of the water and started to the top of the slope again.

"He's such a showoff," mumbled Lennie to himself.

Penelope eagerly
watched Pete's every move as
he prepared himself for a daring
backwards slide.

Pam watched in amazement. "He's already slid
down frontwards and sideways!" she exclaimed.

Penelope giggled and looked at Pete, whose beak
was held high in the air.

Lennie ruffled his feathers and said, "Oh, yeah?
Well, I'll bet he hasn't slid down on his head!"

Everybody snickered. "Nobody can do that!"
said Pete.

"Well, I'll bet I can . . . if I want to,"
bragged Lennie.

"Wow! Can you really, Lennie?" asked Penelope
eagerly.

"Well . . . uh . . . sure I can." He looked
thoughtfully at the icy slope.

"Why don't you try it then?" dared Pete.

"Okay, I will!" he quacked out suddenly, and he waddled to the top of the slope. Lennie found a level place where he could balance himself on his head and his flippers. Carefully he readied himself. The ice glistened below his head, and the gulls circled far above his toes. All the other penguins waited, holding their breath.

"Here I go!" said Lennie as he shoved off with his flippers. Whoosh! He started to gain speed as he struggled to keep his balance. Then whap! His beak caught a pit in the ice, and he flipped and tumbled all the rest of the way down, belly-smacking into the water.

"Is he all right?" asked Pete. Everyone watched with concern.

Slowly Lennie climbed onto the ice. "Yeah, I'm okay," he mumbled.

With a sigh of relief, everyone started to laugh. Even the sky seemed filled with giggling gulls.

Two of the gulls, Stefan and Sebastian, whom Lennie knew all too well, flew down to taunt him. "That's the funniest thing I've ever seen," gasped Stefan.

"You penguins are so silly," laughed Sebastian. "You can't fly, so you slide on your heads and stick your feet toward the clouds!"

"Ha, ha, ha! Now that you've learned how to land on an icy runway, maybe you can take to the air like a real bird!" squawked Stefan. Then he swooped down the icy slope and pretended to crash-land at the end. Again the sky roared with laughing gulls. But his penguin friends weren't laughing anymore. Pete came over to Lennie and said, "Come on, Lennie. We're all going home."

Lennie, his feathers ruffled all over his body, started away. Stefan flew in front of him to tease him again. "You look like you could take off into the clouds right now, Leonard!" he said with a smirk. Lennie swung at him with his flipper, but Stefan flapped into the air to avoid his reach.

Lennie's swing made him spin around on the ice like a ballerina. "Ha, ha, ha, ha!" The gulls' laughter was deafening.

"Just wait! I'll fly even better than you someday, Stefan!" Lennie shouted, and then he waddled away with his friends.

That night Mrs. Penguin served a delicious meal of fishcakes and ice cream, but Lennie hardly ate a thing. "Are you sure you don't want any more?" his mom asked.

"Yes, that's plenty," Lennie replied, though his stomach said otherwise.

"The first thing I've got to do in order to fly is to lose some weight," Lennie told himself. After supper he went straight to his bedroom.

"The second thing I've got to do is to make my wings stronger," he thought. There on the slippery floor he did five pushups, which is not an easy job for a penguin.

The next morning, Lennie did not go sliding as he usually did. Instead, he and Pete went to another side of the iceberg to do some exploring. Lennie knew that the sea hawks flew over there, and he hoped he could find some of their feathers.

"The third thing I need to do in order to fly," he thought, "is to get some bigger feathers."

144

As they waddled together along the edge of the iceberg, Pete said, "Pam and Penelope both said you were very brave even to try sliding down the slope on your head. They're sorry you fell."

He grumbled, "No . . . they just think I'm a clumsy ball of blubber. But I'll show them. I'll show everybody when I fly circles around Stefan someday."

"Listen, Lennie, that's impossible," Pete protested. "Penguins weren't meant to fly; and besides, you're already the best slider and swimmer around here. Nobody cares that you can't fly."

"Well, I care. So just help me find some more sea hawk feathers, okay? I'll show you all . . . someday."

"Okay, Lennie," Pete sighed. He continued looking for feathers. "Hey, there's a big one out in the water," he cried.

Lennie's eyes widened. "Just what I need." He smiled and dove into the water and swam toward the feather. When he was just about next to it, the feather was suddenly rocketed up into the air by a blast of water.

"Hey, what was that?" yelled Pete from the shore. Before Lennie could even make a guess, a gigantic blue whale came to the surface.

"Wha—what are you?" cried the frightened penguin.

"Why, I'm Barnabas Blue Whale. Nice to meet you," the whale boomed.

"Y-you don't eat penguins, d-do you, Mr. Whale?" said Lennie.

"No, I don't," the whale replied. "You don't eat whales, do you?"

"Of course not," chuckled Lennie with a sigh. The hawk feather floated down and landed on the penguin's head. "There it is," he giggled. "That's what I was after when you blew it into the sky."

"I'm very sorry," the whale apologized, "but I couldn't hold my breath much longer. What would you want with a sea hawk feather anyway, Mr. . . . uh . . . ."

"Penguin. Lennie Penguin," Lennie answered. "Well, you see, I'm going to need that when I learn to fly."

"You're going to fly?"

"Yes, better than any sea gull," quacked Lennie. "Especially Stefan."

"Oh, really?"

"Yes. I'll be the only flying penguin in Antarctica!" smiled Lennie.

"What makes you think flying is so important?" the whale asked. "I've never flown anywhere. Swimming suits me fine—and you look like a pretty fair swimmer yourself."

"But whales weren't meant to fly, Barnabas, like pen—well, uh . . ."

"I think I understand now," said the whale with a gleam in his eye. And with that, he took a deep breath and disappeared under the water.

"Bye . . ." But Barnabas was already gone, so Lennie swam to shore with his feather to tell Pete what the whale had said.

For one whole week Lennie did his pushups, didn't eat too much, and collected sea hawk feathers. "As hungry as I am, I must weigh only half as much as I did last week," he thought.

One morning he decided to look for one or two more feathers. As he waddled toward Pete's house, he caught a glimpse of Penelope coming down the street. He put a flipper over his eyes and hoped she wouldn't see him.

"Lennie!" It was Penelope all right. "We've missed you down at the slope lately. Are you coming sliding with us today?"

"No, I don't think so." he replied.

"I'm sorry that you fell last week," she said softly. "We shouldn't have dared you."

Lennie swallowed hard. "Oh . . . that's okay."

Suddenly another voice squawked, "Yes, Leonard, we're so-o-o sorry. Ha, ha, ha." It was Stefan! "Would you like to come flying with us today, Leonard? Ha, ha," the seagull taunted. "Maybe you can fly on your head!"

Lennie gritted his teeth and swung his flipper at Stefan with all his might. The sea gull flew out of the way again, and Lennie somersaulted into the snow bank.

"See you in the clouds, Leonard," squawked Stefan as he flew away.

Lennie didn't eat a bit of lunch that day. He was more determined than ever that he was going to fly. As soon as his mother left for the store, Lennie started toward the far side of the iceberg where the great cliff awaited him. It was the steepest slope around, dropping straight down to the water over a hundred feet below. "That's where I'll learn to fly," thought Lennie as he waddled steadily forward. He passed by Pete's house on the way.

"Hey, Lennie, where are you going?" Pete called.

"Flying," replied Lennie.

"Can't you just try it right here?" Pete asked.

"Nope, I'm going to the great cliff on the other side of the iceberg," Lennie said.

"But that's too dangerous, Lennie. What if you can't fly?"

"I'll fly. Just leave me alone!" Lennie snapped.

After almost half an hour Lennie arrived at the bottom of the great cliff. It was much taller than he had remembered. For a minute he hesitated, but then he muttered to himself, "I'm going to fly," and he started climbing up the snow path to the top. It was a hard path to climb. With each step the icy wind blew colder, till the tips of his flippers were numb.

Finally Lennie arrived at the edge of the cliff. There below him was a small, icy shore sinking into the deep blue ocean. "As long as I get a good running start, I'll still hit the water, even if I can't fly," he thought. But what if he didn't? The very thought of hitting the icy bank almost took his breath away. "B-but I'm going to fly anyway," Lennie reminded himself out loud. He waddled back from the edge, did one last pushup, sucked in his belly, and strapped the sea hawk feathers to his flippers. Then he stood silently, ready for flight, ten steps from the edge of the cliff.

He stood, and he stood, and then he stood a little bit longer.

The shrill cry of a distant sea gull reminded him of Stefan. Wings spread, he ran toward the edge and jumped.

Maybe he hadn't jumped hard enough. Maybe he hadn't lost enough weight. Maybe he hadn't collected enough feathers. But he knew one thing for sure—he was falling faster and faster toward the icy bank below.

Suddenly—splash!—had he hit the water? No, it was more like the water had hit him—a spout of water from Barnabas the Whale! Barnabas kept spouting out water until he had lowered Lennie slowly and safely to the bottom of the cliff.

"Pete!" cried Lennie. Pete sat smiling on the blue whale's back.

"I was worried about you, Lennie, so I went to find Barnabas."

"Oh, thank you both!" sighed Lennie.

"No problem, Mr. Penguin," replied Barnabas, who was a little blue in the face from having spouted for so long, "but next time I might not make it in time."

"There won't be a next time, Barnabas." Lennie answered, feeling very ashamed of himself.

Lennie and Pete rode on the blue whale's back as he swam back toward town. Lennie didn't say very much.

"Will you come out sliding with us tomorrow?" asked Pete. "You really are the best slider around."

"I bet Penelope doesn't think so," replied Lennie, "and I know Stefan doesn't think I can do anything right."

"Don't worry about Stefan," said Pete. "It doesn't matter what he thinks."

Barnabas glided along through the cool, quiet water with his two penguin friends on his back. His blue tail made swelling waves that seemed to tickle him as he swam. Every once in a while he blew a spray of water high into the air.

Lennie asked him, "Barnabas, why do you do that?"

"Do what?" answered the whale.

"Why do you spout as high as you do?" Lennie asked again.

Barnabas thought for a minute. Then he said, "Oh, I guess it's just because I enjoy being a whale so much . . . and that's what whales were meant to do."

Just then Pete saw a gull gliding gently toward them. It was squawking, and it was laughing—and it was Stefan.

"Leonard, ha, ha, ha," cried Stefan. "Where did you get those lovely sea hawk feathers? Ha, ha. Have you been out flying?"

The gull landed right in front of Lennie. Stefan grinned his ugly grin and snickered.

"No, Stefan," replied Lennie without even a twitch of his flipper. "I haven't been flying, and I won't be needing these feathers anymore. You can have them if you'd like."

Stefan's grin faded. "Me? Need feathers? I can fly with what I've got. You're the one that needs them!"

"Penguins don't need to fly," answered Lennie, "and I enjoy being a penguin!" He smiled at Pete, who smiled back. Barnabas spouted higher than ever, sending Stefan flying away with a squawk and a frown on his big yellow bill.

David Livingstone:
Man of Determination

One of the first white men to explore the interior of Africa was an English missionary doctor. He wanted to open up Africa to missions. During his explorations he preached the gospel to many Africans.

Exploring is usually a search for riches. *David Livingstone explored because he was determined to take* riches, *the* riches *of the gospel.*

Determined to Learn

"David," Mrs. Livingstone whispered. "Time to get up."

Ten-year-old David stretched, then crawled out from under the blankets.

"Five o'clock, sleepyhead," his mother said. "You don't want to be late for work your first day."

David dressed quickly, trying not to waken the younger children asleep all around the one-room apartment. Father worked hard as a tea merchant, but his pay was not enough for his big family to live on. The money that David could earn would help to buy the food for the family.

After a quick breakfast, David left for the cotton factory. Oh, how he wished he were on his way to school instead! But from now on he could go to school only late at night after work.

Monday through Saturday David walked along the row of spinning spools. He watched the big frames for thinning threads. It was his job to piece them together before they broke. David's feet were sore from walking and climbing over and under the spinning frames from six o'clock in the morning to eight o'clock at night. His head throbbed with the echo of the clattering machines.

When he received his first pay, David ran home excitedly. Mother stood quietly as he handed her the money. Tears glistened in her eyes. She placed some of the money back in David's hand.

"David, you keep part of this. Buy what you wish," she said.

Eagerly David ran to the bookstore. There on the shelf was the book he wanted!

The storekeeper looked at David. "Are you sure that is the book you want?" he asked.

"Oh, yes sir," David answered.

"Can you read Latin?" the man asked.

"No, sir," said David.

The storekeeper looked puzzled. "Why not get a book you can read?"

"That would be too easy. I want a book to study," David replied.

At first David almost gave up. But in his spare time he studied hard. He was determined to learn Latin.

The other children at work did not understand David's love for learning. He often took a book to work and balanced it on the spinning jenny. Each time he came past the book he read a minute before continuing his walk along the frames. Sometimes the boys tried to knock his book down by throwing thread bobbins at it, but when they did, David just put the book back up and kept on studying.

Every night David left the factory tired. But every night he went to school until ten o'clock.

"I hope I can finish this science book tonight," David thought as he walked home in the moonlight.

Mother met him at the door. The one-room apartment was silent; the other children were asleep in their beds on the floor. David ate his porridge and quietly studied by the light from the lamp. The next two hours were his study time.

At about midnight David's mother awoke. "It's late, David. Morning will come quickly."

David hadn't quite finished the book, but he put out the lamp and climbed wearily into his bed.

David received some training at home and at Sabbath school as well. His father was a Sabbath-school teacher and a member of a missionary society. As a young boy David memorized long Bible passages.

But as David read more and more books, he began to like science very much. When he had a little spare time, he collected herbs and rocks. Science became very important to him. As time went on, he began to feel that the Bible and science did not agree. He did not have peace about the things his father had taught him.

When he was a young man, David's determination to learn finally brought him to the truth. He read a book that helped him to see that science backs up the Bible and that they do not go against each other. At that time he accepted Christ's salvation for himself.

Determined to Tell

As time went on David knew that the Lord wanted him to become a missionary doctor.

Although the Livingstones were still very poor, David began saving what he could. Others at work did not understand David's goal. They too worked hard but had little money.

"You'll never have enough money to go to the university. Give up!" The men laughed at David.

"I'll not give up studying. Someday I'll go to the university," David said aloud.

Four years later, David finally had enough money to start at the university. First he would learn to preach; then he would become a doctor.

One day he heard a preacher who had worked in Africa. "Africa needs the Word of God," Mr. Moffat said. "I have seen the smoke of a thousand villages, villages where no white man has ever gone!"

"I will go there," Dr. Livingstone said in his heart. "I will take God's message to the people of Africa."

David finished his training. The Livingstone family had one final evening together before David was to leave.

"We should stay up and talk all night," David told his family.

Of course his mother didn't agree to that. "No, David, you need your rest to travel."

"We'll get up early and read the Bible together," his father said.

At five o'clock the next morning, they gathered to read the Scripture. " 'The Lord shall preserve thee from all evil; he shall preserve thy soul, ' " David read.

Each head bowed as Father led in prayer. Then in turn the other family members prayed for David. As they later said good-bye to him, they wondered if they would ever see him again.

On November 17, 1840, David Livingstone left his home in England to serve the Lord in Africa.

Dr. Livingstone arrived at the mission station that was the home of Mr. Moffat and his family. Livingstone's first task in Africa was to learn a new language. So he moved away from the mission to live in the jungle. There he learned the ways and language of the natives.

Then Livingstone set out to visit tribes that had never heard of God. They listened to him tell about God. They listened to the hymns he sang. They were fascinated by the "magic lantern" slide pictures that he showed. Yet only God could reach their hearts.

One chief sent a messenger to Dr. Livingstone inviting the doctor to his tribe. But when Dr. Livingstone arrived, the chief refused to talk. He found some women crying beside a hut. "The chief's only son is sick," the women cried.

Dr. Livingstone knew that his medicine might help the boy. But he also knew that if the medicine failed, the people would be very angry. Then they might not want to hear about God.

"Lord," Dr. Livingstone prayed, "show me what to do."

God gave Dr. Livingstone courage to try his medicine on the boy. The chief allowed the doctor to see his sick son. Dr. Livingstone gave the boy some medicine and waited.

The next morning the chief's son was able to sit up and eat. He had begun to get well.

"Why do you come?" the chief asked. "I have heard of white men who come to our coast for ivory or slaves."

"I came to tell you about God, Who loves you," Dr. Livingstone replied.

Another tribe that Dr. Livingstone tried to reach had a different problem. Many lions had been destroying their sheep, cattle, goats, and sometimes even people.

"Why don't you kill the lions?" Dr. Livingstone asked the people.

"The lions have evil spirits in them," a native answered.

The doctor shook his head. "These lions are like any others," he said. "They don't have evil spirits. The lions are part of God's creation, but man is more important to God. We must not let the lions hurt your people. If we kill one great lion, the others may flee to another valley."

One day a native messenger came running to David. "Lions are attacking the sheep," he called.

David grabbed his gun and ran with the native toward the village. He shouted to the frightened villagers to kill the lion. He thought they would follow his example and help him against the lion. When they moved back, shaking their heads, he fired both barrels of his gun at the lion.

The lion seemed unhurt. Livingstone began to reload his gun. The lion turned and leaped

on the missionary, biting his shoulder. Just in time a native friend fired at the lion. Then the fierce lion turned on the doctor's friend. Another native tried to help. He too was hurt by the lion. At last the lion fell and died.

The men were taken back to the station to be treated. There was no doctor to help. Dr. Livingstone had to give instructions to others. His arm was hurt very badly, but his helpers were able to set it in such a way that it did heal. In the years of travel and hard work that followed, he was able to use the arm even though it never looked the same again.

The next year Dr. Livingstone married Mary Moffat, who had grown up on her father's mission station. For several years David and Mary worked together, teaching and training natives and rearing a family.

Determined to Find

Dr. Livingstone was burdened for the tribes in the north. He also knew that Africa needed a mission to train the natives. He was determined to find a place in the north to build that mission. After making several exploration trips with his family, Dr. Livingstone learned that there was a danger in the jungle far worse than lions. That danger was fever. Often his wife and children became ill. If Dr. Livingstone had not known medicine himself, they could not have survived.

"I must find a place in central Africa where missionaries can live in good health," he wrote to the mission board. "Then we can bring many missionaries to help teach the African Christians."

So he sent his wife and children back to England and turned to the task of finding a good place to build a mission. For years he explored Africa. As he traveled, he kept on preaching the gospel, but he knew that he had to make it possible for some other missionaries to come. He kept careful journals, made maps, collected samples of rocks and plants, and sent letters to his friends in England.

When he went home to England for a visit, he was surprised to find that people were very interested in what he had to say. He was honored and asked to write books and make speeches. The books he wrote helped him to raise money. Part of the money was left for his older children, and part of it was used to get supplies for his next trip into Africa. The biggest thing he bought was a steamboat. With the help of a boat, Dr. Livingstone felt that he could save time and soon establish a home again.

He took his wife and youngest child back to Africa with him. His wife was ill when they got to Africa, so he left her and his child at the Moffat mission station.

He was more determined than ever to find a spot for a mission station in the north. When the steamboat arrived, Dr. Livingstone and his party got ready. They loaded the steamboat with supplies and started out. But it was not as easy as Dr. Livingstone had hoped.

"Why are we stopping?" Dr. Livingstone called to the navigator.

"Fuel!" came the answer. "This engine needs a lot of fuel; we are all out again." For several days the exploring party had to wait while ebony and other hard wood were found to feed the engine. It took a day and a half to find enough fuel to travel one day.

Finally, after the clumsy engine was heated up again, the boat made another start. A few miles up the river when the travelers had picked up all the speed they could get, a group of natives in canoes paddled up stream by them. They had never seen a big boat. "Is your boat all cut out of one big tree?" they asked. But they paddled right by, leaving the slow-moving steamboat behind.

"Look, Dr. Livingstone. They are able to pass us," shouted a helper over the din of the engine.

"The next boat I bring to Africa will be better," Dr. Livingstone called back.

But even though a better boat was made available to Dr. Livingstone at a later time, the uncharted rivers had many rapids and shifting sand bars. After several years the idea of using boats was given up.

This was a sad time for Dr. Livingstone in another way. During the years of river exploration his wife had become ill and returned to Scotland. When she finally got back to Africa, she had been with Livingstone only a short time when she died.

Dr. Livingstone was still determined. He made a trip back to England to visit his children and to raise more funds. Then he returned to Africa with a new idea. He was sure that if he could find the headwaters of the big Nile River he would open up a passage into Africa. He thought that if a good trade could be made possible, the slave dealers could be stopped, and Christian missionaries could get in.

This time Livingstone selected a party of all natives and started out on foot. Again he preached, kept journals, and gathered information. Two big problems made Dr. Livingstone's work hard. Arab slave dealers were causing great trouble for the natives, and many of Livingstone's helpers ran away.

One group of natives ran away and got safely back to the coast. Since they didn't want to get in trouble for deserting the exploring party, they told lies.

"He is dead," the natives told Dr. Livingstone's friends.

"We were attacked by savages," one explained.

"I hid in the bushes and saw it all," another one lied.

Sad letters were written to England.

The news headlines announced, "David Livingstone is dead." People again became very interested in David Livingstone. Some did not believe the story. Others felt that Dr. Livingstone's body should be found and brought back to England.

An American newspaper sent an Englishman named Stanley to lead a search. This brave man looked for Livingstone for a long time. When Stanley finally found Livingstone, Arab slave dealers had stolen all of Livingstone's supplies. He was sick and needed help very badly. The two men camped together for several months. Dr. Livingstone was grateful to have an Englishman to talk to after six years. Stanley's good food and medical supplies brought Livingstone back to better health. While they lived together, Stanley watched Livingstone as he taught and preached to the natives.

Stanley wrote in his journal:

His gentleness never forsakes him,
his hopefulness never deserts him.

Stanley was not able to persuade the determined Dr. Livingstone to return to England with him.

Livingstone kept on trying to find the headwaters of the Nile. He became ill again and was cared for by the natives he loved until he died.

Dr. Livingstone never found the headwaters of the Nile, but his exploring and writings made it possible for other missionaries to get into Africa with the riches of the gospel.

Esther, the Queen

After the days of King Solomon, God's people became more and more disobedient. The judgment of God brought mighty nations to capture Israel and to carry away many people to faraway lands. Even though God allowed His people to be punished, He was watchful and protected them. The following account adapted from the book of Esther clearly shows God's protecting hand on His people, the Jews.

The King's House

Esther was just finishing her weaving when Mordecai came running in with the latest news from the palace.

"I have heard," he said, "that the queen has made King Ahasuerus angry. The stories say that he will be sending her away."

Esther gasped. "Send away Queen Vashti? But who will be our queen?"

"There are rumors . . . but I do not know if they are true." Mordecai hesitated. "The rumors say that he will be looking for a new wife among the beautiful young girls of his lands."

The stories Mordecai had heard were true. Announcements were posted the next day. Officers came to all the homes in all the far corners of King Ahasuerus's lands. They took lovely girls back to the palace. Esther was among them. She thanked God that Mordecai lived near the palace. There was still a chance that she might see him sometimes.

Esther remembered what Mordecai had told her. "Do not tell anyone that you are a Jewess," he had said. "And do not tell that you are my cousin." Esther obeyed him and breathed not a word of her background.

Hegai was in charge of all the women. There were princesses who had been brought from far away. There were humble shepherdesses and village girls whose eyes were dazzled by the beauty and splendor of the palace. What noise and confusion there were!

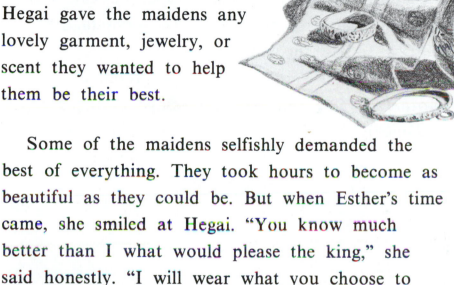

As time passed, Hegai took the beautiful maidens one by one to see the king. Hegai gave the maidens any lovely garment, jewelry, or scent they wanted to help them be their best.

Some of the maidens selfishly demanded the best of everything. They took hours to become as beautiful as they could be. But when Esther's time came, she smiled at Hegai. "You know much better than I what would please the king," she said honestly. "I will wear what you choose to give me."

Hegai was pleased. "Esther is a sensible girl," he thought.

Hegai spent more time carefully arranging her clothes and fixing her hair than he had spent on any of the other women. When he had finished, even the other women had to admit that Esther was beautiful.

"I am sure that you will please the king, Esther," Hegai said.

Esther did not regret letting Hegai choose her apparel. The king chose her, over all the other women, to be his queen.

But Esther still didn't tell anyone that she was a Jewess.

Mordecai was serving at the palace gate. Sometimes he heard people whispering. One day someone whispered to him, "Two servants are plotting to kill the king!"

"I must tell Esther about this," thought Mordecai. "She can take a message to the king."

Quickly Mordecai wrote a note and gave it to a messenger. "Deliver this to your queen immediately," he instructed.

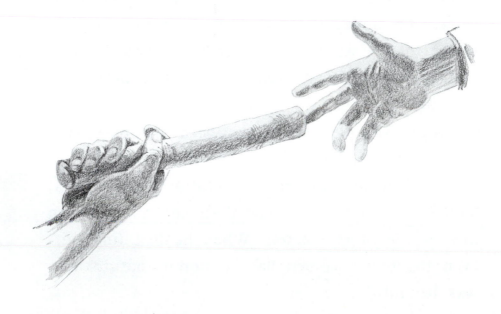

When Esther read the letter, she realized that King Ahasuerus was in great danger. When the king sent for her, Esther showed him Mordecai's message.

"What is this? Servants are plotting to kill me?" Ahasuerus roared in his rage. "I am the most powerful king on earth, and they plot to kill me?"

Quickly King Ahasuerus sent spies to investigate the plot to kill him. They found out that what the man Mordecai had said was true.

"Hang both of the men," King Ahasuerus ordered. "We will show how dangerous it is to plot to kill a king." Turning to his scribe, he said, "Write of this matter in the chronicles of the king."

Then Ahasuerus took Esther's hand. "You honor your king," he said. "You have helped to save my life."

Haman's Plot

In the kingdom there lived a prince named Haman. Haman knew just how to please King Ahasuerus. The king promoted him to be chief of all the princes. Now only the king himself was more important than Haman.

Haman liked to see all the servants bowing down to him. "I am a very important man," he thought. "Everyone honors me."

But Esther's cousin, Mordecai, would not bow down to Haman. The other servants whispered, "Mordecai, that is Haman! The king has commanded that we bow to him. Why do you not do it?"

Mordecai replied, "I am a Jew. I worship only the one true God."

Day after day Mordecai refused to bow. The other servants didn't understand why he wouldn't bow with them. Finally they told Haman about Mordecai.

The next day when Haman marched through the gate, he searched the crowds of people. There, off to the side, he saw Mordecai. Mordecai did not bow or even stand up. "What are you doing?" Haman shouted. "Do you not know that I am Haman, the chief of all the princes?"

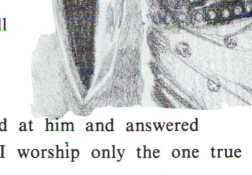

Mordecai just looked at him and answered quietly. "I am a Jew. I worship only the one true God."

Haman turned pale with anger and stalked away.

"I will kill Mordecai," he thought. "And I will kill all the other Jews too. Then there will not be anyone who will refuse to bow down to me."

The next day Haman went before the king. "There is a people in your land," he said, "that do not believe the same way you do. They do not keep your laws. You should have them destroyed. All you need to do is write the decree. I will handle the rest of it."

King Ahasuerus trusted Haman so much that he agreed. "If you think that is best, Haman, you may use whatever you need to do it." He gave Haman his ring as a sign of permission.

Filled with evil glee, Haman rushed to send out the message. Throughout all the lands the news was posted:

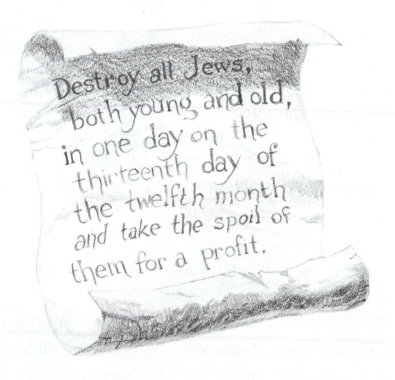

Destroy all Jews, both young and old, in one day on the thirteenth day of the twelfth month and take the spoil of them for a profit.

When the Jews learned of the decree, they tore their clothes and mourned loudly. They dressed themselves in sackcloth and put ashes on their heads, praying that the Lord God would save them.

Queen Esther didn't know about the decree until a servant came with the news. "The man Mordecai stands outside the king's gate in sackcloth and ashes," he told the queen.

"Something is dreadfully wrong," Esther said as she quickly gathered some clothes. "Take these to him," she said. "Tell him to put them on."

But the servant returned. "Mordecai would not put on the clothes," he said.

Esther quickly called for a trusted messenger. "I must know why Mordecai is mourning," she said. "Please find out for me."

The messenger returned from the king's gate. "Mordecai tells me that Haman has commanded that all the Jews be destroyed," he said. "Here is proof of it." He held up the copy of the decree that Mordecai had given him. "Mordecai says you must go to the king and beg for the lives of your people."

Esther gasped. "I cannot! The only time I can go before the king is when he sends for me. He has not sent for me for thirty days. If I go before him and he does not hold out his golden scepter, that will mean death for me!"

Again Mordecai sent a message. "Esther, if you do not speak to the king, the Lord will deliver His people anyway, but you will be punished. Who knows but that you may have become queen just for such a time as this?"

Esther sighed. "Send this message to Mordecai," she said. "Tell all the Jews to fast and pray for me for three days and three nights. At the end of that time I will go to the king, even though it may mean my death. But if I perish, I perish."

Mordecai did everything Esther said. He prayed, all the other Jews prayed, and Esther prayed for guidance and wisdom. Esther also prayed that the Lord would prepare the king's heart.

A Banquet for Three

At the end of three days, Esther prepared to go before the king. She dressed just as she knew the king liked for her to dress. She walked slowly through the courtyard and through the inner court. There, in the royal house, she could see King Ahasuerus sitting on his throne. When he looked up and saw Esther, he frowned. Esther felt her heart beating hard.

"Oh, God of my fathers," she whispered, "be with me now. Give me wisdom in my actions and in my words."

Esther stood in the doorway, her head bowed low in reverence to the king. King Ahasuerus watched the queen. He knew that she was facing death to approach him. The servants dared not breathe.

Then the king held out the golden scepter for her to touch, his sign that he accepted her.

The servants sighed with relief. Esther sighed gently too and smiled as she approached her husband.

Ahasuerus smiled back at her. "What is your request, Queen Esther? I will give you whatever you want."

Esther spoke softly. "If it please you, Your Majesty," she said, "I would like to invite Your Majesty and Haman to a banquet."

The king listened in amazement. Esther had risked her life for this! Quickly he called his servants. "Tell Haman that Queen Esther is having a banquet for us. Tell him to come immediately."

When Haman heard the message, he clapped his hands together in delight. An invitation to eat with the king and the queen! He hurried to Esther's banquet as quickly as he could walk.

King Ahasuerus enjoyed the banquet so much that he said, "Esther, whatever you want, I will give you. Just ask."

Still Esther was careful. "I would like for you and Haman to come to another banquet tomorrow night."

Haman was delighted. "I am the favorite of the king," he thought to himself as he left the palace. "And I am the favorite of the queen! Who is nobler than Haman? No one! No one!"

As Haman passed through the gates, he smiled to himself. All the people were bowing, as always.

But . . . there was Mordecai! Still he would not bow. Haman clenched his fists. He forgot all the exciting things that had happened to him. All he could think about was this man Mordecai.

With effort Haman kept himself from doing anything to Mordecai just then. He went home as fast as he could and called everyone around.

"Listen to me," he said. "I have been honored above all men! The queen held a banquet for the king tonight, and I was the only other one invited. Moreover, she is holding another banquet for me tomorrow night!" Haman stood tall and proud.

All his friends and family stood speechless with wonder. No one they had ever known had received such an honor.

"But still . . ." Haman's face suddenly turned red with anger, "this doesn't satisfy me as long as I see the man Mordecai sitting at the gate."

"You are letting this Mordecai ruin your happiness." Haman's wife shook her finger at him. "You are not just anyone. You are the chief of the princes. You are the one who went to the queen's banquet. You are Haman! Do not let Mordecai distress you. This very night, command that a tall gallows be built, taller than any in the land. Tomorrow ask the king's permission to hang Mordecai on that gallows. Everyone knows that the king will do anything you suggest, Haman. Then you can enjoy the banquet with a merry heart."

Haman's eyes narrowed into slits. "Yes," he said. "Of course. I will do that very thing!"

Rescue

That night the king couldn't sleep. He commanded that a servant bring in something to read to him.

The servant read from the chronicles of the king. For hours his sleepy voice droned on and on. King Ahasuerus still lay awake. Then as morning began to dawn, the servant read a very interesting story. It was about two men who had plotted to kill the king. The man Mordecai had reported it and had saved the king's life.

King Ahasuerus sat up in his bed. "I remember that. Read to me what has been done for this noble man. I am sure it was something great." "There is no record that anything has been done," the servant replied. "Mordecai was never rewarded."

"Never rewarded?" King Ahasuerus said slowly. "How did that happen? I must surely do something for him." He looked around, thinking he heard a noise in the outer court. "Who is there?"

"It is Haman, Your Majesty," the servant answered. "He has come to see Your Majesty on urgent business."

"Send him in immediately. I have some important business to discuss with him too."

Haman came bustling into the king's bedroom. He was eager to ask if he could hang Mordecai. He wanted to hurry and get the hanging over with early so that he could enjoy the banquet that night.

But before he could speak a word of request, King Ahasuerus said, "Haman, what will I do for a man I am delighted to honor?"

Haman felt lightheaded and dizzy. He thought to himself, "The king must want to honor me. Who else could it be? This will be the most glorious day of my life." Then he spoke his wish, a wish he had been dreaming of for some time.

"Your Majesty, if you delight to honor a special man, this is my suggestion. Give him your cloak to wear and your horse to ride, and put your crown upon his head. Then send one of the most noble princes to lead this special man on horseback through the city. The noble prince will shout before him, 'This is what will be done for the man that the king delights to honor!' "

King Ahasuerus smiled. "That is an excellent idea. And since you are my most noble prince, you are the one who will do it. Hurry and do this very thing for Mordecai the Jew. Be sure to do all that you suggested."

Mordecai! Haman tried hard not to let the king see the look on his face. Now he could never ask permission to hang Mordecai on the gallows. Never!

Haman quickly left the palace. For fear of his life, he did everything the king had told him to do. He gave Mordecai the royal cloak, the royal horse, and the royal crown. And then Haman went through the street shouting, "This is what will be done for the man that the king delights to honor!"

Then Haman ran home, mourning loudly over what had happened.

"This is not a good sign," his wife said. "If this happened with Mordecai the Jew, it is a sign that something worse is going to happen."

"Something worse!" Haman shouted. "Nothing could possibly happen that is any worse than what happened to me today."

As he was speaking, the king's servant came in to remind him of Queen Esther's banquet. Haman hurried away.

That evening, just as the evening before, King Ahasuerus asked Queen Esther what he could do for her.

"O King," Esther answered, "if it pleases you, let my life and the lives of my people be spared. There is a wicked man planning to kill us."

King Ahasuerus felt shocked and angry that someone would try to kill his queen. "Who is this man that dares plot such a thing?" he asked.

"My enemy and the enemy of all my people is this wicked Haman!" Esther's finger pointed straight at the astonished man.

Haman—the king's favorite! King Ahasuerus was so upset that he left the room without a word.

Haman collapsed in terror. He had not known that Queen Esther was a Jewess. Now he remembered his wife's dark words and begged Queen Esther to spare his life.

The king returned and, full of anger, shouted at Haman. A servant said, "Haman has built a gallows where he is planning to hang Mordecai."

"He wants to hang Mordecai, the man who saved my life? That is enough. Hang Haman on that gallows."

So Haman was hanged. Then King Ahasuerus did what was needed to rescue the Jews. The appointed day became a day of feasting and gladness instead of a day of death and mourning.

Mordecai was made the chief of all the princes, the very position that Haman used to have. Esther had been made the queen "for such a time as this."

DAYS TO REMEMBER

A TICKET TO THE

CIRCUS

How would you like to be the shortest nine-year-old boy around? Richy certainly doesn't. But when the circus comes to town, he learns that being short has its advantages after all!

It was Richy's job to tend the family garden, so he had been pulling weeds all afternoon. He had weeded everything except the tomatoes when his mother called him to the house. She met him on the back porch with a glass of lemonade in one hand and a nickel in the other. "I've been mending a pair of your father's socks and have run out of darning floss. Esther is napping, and supper is on the stove, so I need you to run to the general store for me. It closes early on Saturday, so you'll have to hurry."

Richy exchanged his empty glass for the coin and disappeared around the side of the house. With the speed and accuracy that come with practice, Richy hurdled a peony bush and did cartwheels all the way to the shed. He rolled out his bike and raced off down the street to the general store.

He took the steps up to the store two at a time, swung the screen door open, and stopped. Never had he seen so many people there at one time! No one seemed to be shopping. Everyone was just milling around, chattering excitedly. Richy found his way to the counter and stood there patiently, but no one noticed him, not even the clerk behind the counter.

"Pardon me, sir," Richy began, "but I've come to buy some darning floss for my mother." Silence. Richy cleared his throat quite loudly. Still no response. Richy flinched at the thought, but he knew he would have to ding the little counter bell if he were to make his purchase before closing time. Ding! The clerk glanced from side to side with a curious expression on his face.

"Down here, sir," said Richy sheepishly.

"Ah, yes, Richy, didn't see you there. And what'll it be today?"

"Some darning floss for my mother, please."

"All righty. That'll be three cents, please."

Richy paid the man and asked, "What's all the excitement about?"

"Haven't you heard? The circus is coming to town!"

"The circus! When?"

"Next month. August 10th to be exact. I'm surprised you haven't seen the posters. Some men from the circus were in town this afternoon putting them up."

Richy thanked the man for his help, stuffed the darning floss and change in his pocket, and raced outside. Everywhere he looked there were huge colorful posters describing the many wonders of the circus and proclaiming Friday, August 10, 1928, as the date of the show. Richy fairly flew home with the good news!

He sped up the driveway on his back wheel, yelling, "The circus is coming!"

Little Esther caught the circus spirit right away and marched around the house tooting an imaginary horn. Mother began counting the money in the cookie jar. Richy tossed in the two pennies from his pocket and handed his mother the darning floss.

"Mother, can we afford to take the whole family?"

"Not yet, Richy," Mother sighed. "But we'll just save every penny we can and keep darning our socks instead of buying new ones!"

"And I'll sell some fresh vegetables from the garden!" added Richy as he ran outside to finish weeding the tomatoes.

Father went out to the garden as soon as he got home from work. "The garden looks mighty fine, son."

"Thank you, Father."

"By the way, Thomas Betchler stopped by the lumberyard this afternoon. He's with the Betchler Brothers Circus. He said they were looking for strong boys to help set up the circus next month. I told them there was a boy at my house they could count on."

Richy let out a hoot, hugged his father, and did a one-handed flip right there next to the tomatoes.

The entire town was looking forward to the coming of the circus. The children nearly memorized the circus posters. The boys especially liked the lunging tiger with its white fangs and fiery eyes. All the girls were dazzled by the beautifully costumed women riding bareback on pure white horses. The women discussed whether or not the dwarf was the real thing, while the men in town tried to figure out how much it would cost to feed a dozen elephants.

Richy's family was busy finding ways to earn extra money for their circus fund. Mother contributed what she was paid to sew a dress for the lady next door. Father put in the 25-cent tip he got for making a lumber delivery after hours. Even little Esther gave the penny she earned helping the Widow Johnson wash windows.

Richy was counting on selling tomatoes to make his donation to the cookie jar. When the first tomatoes ripened in the warmth of August, he had no trouble selling them because they were beauties.

In fact, sales were so good that when Richy added his money to the circus fund, there was enough to take the Widow Johnson with them. Now August 10th couldn't come soon enough!

Several men from the circus came a day early to make sure everything would be ready for the circus when it arrived. They set up camp at the edge of town in the clearing where the circus would be held and began their work. The needs of both the circus people and the circus animals were considered as they bought food and supplies from the general store and hauled wagonload after wagonload of hay and feed from the mill.

Richy and the other boys could only watch from afar, for their help was not needed until the next day.

In the middle of the night, even as Richy was dreaming about the coming circus, the first circus train arrived. The people on this train, which was called the Flying Squadron, came ahead of the main circus train so they could set up the cookhouse and mark where all the circus tents would be placed.

Richy was part of the crowd that met the main circus train when it pulled in at six o'clock the next morning. From the limb of a nearby tree, Richy watched the unloading begin.

First, steel plates were placed between the railroad cars to form one long bridge. Then teams of horses pulled the circus wagons across the bridge and down a ramp to the ground. It was hard to tell what was in each wagon except for those with "WILD ANIMALS—DANGER—DO NOT TOUCH!" painted on their canvas covers. Some people stayed and watched until all the wagons were off the train, but Richy joined the children who followed the first few wagons to the clearing at the edge of town.

The smell of bacon and eggs greeted the hungry circus company, but breakfast was eaten quickly, and the business of setting up the Betchler Brothers Circus began.

Because all the tent stakes had been laid out in their places, the stake-driving crews picked up their sledgehammers and went right to work. With the combined power of several elephants and dozens of men, the three main poles for the big top were raised. Next the smaller side poles were put on the ground in their proper positions. After Richy and the other boys helped unroll and lace together the pieces of tent canvas, the side poles went up, and the tent looked like a great flat saucer. Then the elephants and men raised the huge tent roof and set the medium-sized poles in place. Finally the tent ropes were tightened, and the big top was ready for the seats to be set up inside.

The boys helped raise the sideshow and
menagerie tents. Then they were divided into two
groups. One group helped feed the horses and
elephants, and Richy's group carried buckets of
water to the circus performers. Richy's group
leader took one look at him and shook his head.
"I'm afraid this bucket is too heavy for a little
fellow like you. I'll have to take it to the Arabian
Princess myself."

"But sir . . ." Richy began, but the man was already walking away. Richy's face got hot, and he felt a lump in his throat.

The man turned back. "Hey, kid, there is something you could do to help. Take this letter to Lou Weaver. He's in the first wagon past the cookhouse."

Letter in hand, Richy started walking slowly toward the cookhouse. He was trying to swallow the lump in his throat at the same time he was trying not to think about the Arabian Princess and that silly bucket of water, but Richy was still in low spirits when he knocked at the door of Lou Weaver's wagon.

"Come in."

Richy opened the door and saw a man sitting behind a large desk. "I have a letter for Lou Weaver."

"That's me. Dr. Louis J. Weaver, the circus crowd-pleaser!" He took the letter and began opening it.

"Are you a clown, Mr. Weaver?"

"I am indeed! But please call me Lou. And who, pray tell, are you?"

"My name is Richy. I'm one of the boys helping set up the circus today. Well, I *was* helping set up until . . ." Richy hesitated. That lump was back in his throat.

"Until what?" Lou asked, setting his letter aside. "You can tell me."

So Richy poured out the whole story, and before long Lou had Richy laughing and smiling again.

"I understand your problem much better than you may think," said Lou, slipping out from behind his desk. Richy was surprised to find himself looking at Lou eye to eye.

"Yes, Richy, I'm a midget. But there's nothing I can do to change that, so I just do my best with what I have. And you know what? I've discovered that there are a lot of things I can do that other folks can't. How many people do you know who can do a one-handed flip?"

"I don't know of anyone but myself."

"So you're an acrobat, Richy! That's wonderful! Why don't you and I go out to the practice area? You can show me a few of your tricks, and I'll show you some of mine." So off they went, and what a grand time they had! Lou taught Richy several new acrobatic stunts. He even taught Richy how to ride a unicycle, which was Lou's big solo act in the circus. They didn't realize how late it was getting until another clown stopped by to remind Lou of their meeting in five minutes. Lou had to rush off to his meeting, and Richy needed to pick up his free pass and hurry home.

Richy got to the ticket wagon just as the last few boys were picking up their passes. Richy got in line behind them, and when it was his turn, the ticket man didn't see him. Down went the little window on the ticket wagon, and Richey was left standing there without his pass to the circus!

When he got home, Richy couldn't bring himself to tell his family what had happened. That evening he got ready to go to the circus as if nothing were wrong and then asked if he might go early. Father winked at Mother and said, "Yes."

Richy raced to the edge of town and headed straight for the ticket wagon. He stood on his toes and spoke as loudly as he could, "Sir, I'm one of the boys who helped set up the circus today. I didn't get my free pass this afternoon, so I'd like to pick it up now, if I may."

"You may not! What proof do I have that they actually put a wee fellow like you to work?"

"You have my word, sir."

"That isn't enough. I need the word of your group leader. Find him and you'll have your free pass. Next."

Richy moved aside for the next person in line and then stood frozen in his tracks. He didn't know where to start looking. He didn't even know the name of his group leader. There was only one person he knew to ask, so Richy made a beeline for the first wagon past the cookhouse. Richy was relieved to see a light inside. He knocked and called out, "Lou, it's Richy. May I come in?"

"Sure, pal. The door's open."

Richy opened the door expecting to see Lou the Clown in his makeup and costume. Instead, Lou was sitting at his desk with his head in his hands. He hadn't even started to get ready.

"Richy, why aren't you with your family?"

"It's a long story. But why aren't you ready for the show? Is something wrong?"

"I finally read that letter you delivered. It's from my sister. She says that my mother is very sick and that I must come home to Kansas at once."

"Why don't you leave on the evening train?"

"I'd like to, Richy, but I have to do tonight's show. They could do without me except for my unicycle act."

"Oh, Lou, I wish there were something I could do to help."

Suddenly Lou jumped from his chair and ran for the door. "Maybe you *can* help! Don't go anywhere. I'll be right back!" True to his word, Lou was back in minutes, and he was all smiles. "Mr. Betchler said it's all right!"

"Lou, what are you talking about?"

"Mr. Betchler said it's all right for you to fill in for my big solo act tonight! I told him you'd make a splendid clown because you're a fine acrobat, because you know how to ride a unicycle, and because you're the right size!"

Richy let out a hoot and did a one-handed flip right there in Lou's wagon.

"Well, what are we waiting for, Richy? We have to get you ready for the show!"

216

Lou seated Richy at his dressing table and began to apply the clown makeup with quick, sure strokes. Richy laughed as a frizzy red wig went on next. Then Lou reached in his trunk and pulled out a costume with bright polka dots and a matching hat. "Here. Put these on while I pack my suitcase."

Richy dressed, taking care not to smear his new face, and stood before the mirror, unbelieving. Lou appeared with his suitcase just as the circus band began to play its first song. "Ah! Perfect timing! Follow me."

Lou gave Richy last-minute instructions as they walked to the big top. "After the lion tamer is through, there will be a drumroll, and the ringmaster will say, 'And now, ladies and gentlemen, Richy the Great, riding his one-wheeled wonder!' That's when you enter and ride around the hippodrome just as I showed you this afternoon."

At the big top a circus worker holding Lou's unicycle was waiting for them.

"Richy, this friend of mine will take you from here. And now I must go." Lou set down his suitcase and gave Richy a big hug. "I wish I could stay and watch your debut, pal; but thanks to you, I have a train to catch!"

Up in the Air

It's 1783. You want to take an exciting ride. What will you choose to ride in? No, you can't go in a rocket, for they haven't been invented yet. How about boarding a sleek silver jet? You forgot again; it's only 1783. Men are not even thinking about jets yet. So what are they dreaming about?

All through history man has dreamed of flying like a bird. Sometimes people even made wings for themselves and tried to fly. They climbed to high places and jumped off.

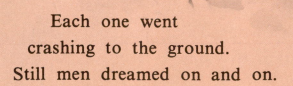

Each one went crashing to the ground. Still men dreamed on and on.

Joseph Montgolfier was one Frenchman who kept dreaming. One day he was thinking about the clouds floating in the air. "Those clouds look like the steam that comes from our kitchen kettle," he said to himself.

Joseph hurried home, put the kettle over the fire, and waited impatiently. As the steam came out, Joseph tried to capture it in a paper bag. The bag fell to the floor.

"Hmmm," Joseph said to his brother and sister, "clouds are like smoke too. Let's fill a paper bag with smoke."

Quickly they threw straw on the kitchen fire. As the smoke rose, the paper bag expanded. The heat of the air in the bag made it rise to the ceiling!

That floating hot-air bag was the beginning of balloons. Now perhaps you're thinking of the brightly colored balloons you get at a circus or fair. You must think larger, like Joseph did. He began to dream of hot-air balloons big enough to carry people.

Much experimenting had to be done before balloons could carry people. In 1783 Joseph made the first real balloon. As a large, excited crowd watched, Joseph filled his silk balloon with hot air. Strong men had to hold the ropes to keep the balloon from floating away.

At last Joseph gave the signal, the men let go, and the balloon floated up! The crowd cheered! The first balloon was off!

The king of France heard about Joseph's balloon and asked him to make a special one. The day finally came when the huge, beautiful balloon was ready. It had a willow basket underneath big enough for someone to ride in.

"No one is going to ride in the balloon," the king ordered. "It's too dangerous."

But the king did allow a sheep, a duck, and a rooster to take the first ride. The balloon took off with the sheep bleating, the duck quacking, and the rooster crowing. When the balloon finally landed, all three animals were found safe and sound. (The rooster did, however, have a broken wing from being kicked by the sheep.)

The success of that balloon made Joseph want to keep on experimenting. He made a balloon as tall as a seven-story building! The big basket underneath had enough room for two men, straw and wool for the fire, and a fire pan. But Joseph didn't want to take the first ride!

Two men volunteered eagerly for the job. One man was to put the straw and wool on the fire. The other man was to be the navigator.

November 21, 1783, and sunny. As the first balloon with men in it took off, all of Paris watched. Women shouted from the windows, men cheered from the rooftops, and children waved from the streets. Higher and higher went the balloon as the men added fuel to the fire. When the men became too interested in watching the scenery, the fire began to die down.

The balloon dropped until the men noticed their
danger. Quickly they threw more fuel on the fire,
and the balloon floated back up into the sky.
Finally, after twenty-five minutes, the supply of
fuel gave out. The balloon floated to the ground.
It had traveled five miles from its launching pad
in Paris.

After that, many people
experimented with balloons.
Some men put oars, sails,
and rudders on their
balloons. That didn't work.

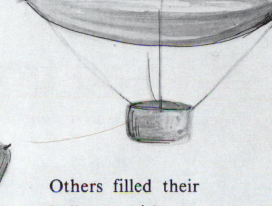

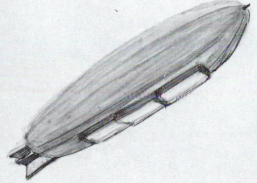

Others filled their
balloons with
hydrogen instead
of hot air. And
that did work.

As time passed, scientists used balloons to
collect information about air currents and the
weather. Generals used hot-air balloons in war to
see where the enemy was. People rode in balloons
just because they were fun! Do you think riding
in a balloon would be fun?

Raised from the Dead

(A choral reading taken from John 11:1-27)

Readers

Boys:	**Girls:**
Boy 1: Narrator	**Girl A:** Narrator
Boy 2: Jesus	**Girl B:** Martha
Boys Chorus	**Girl C:** Mary
	Girls Chorus

Boy 1: Now a certain man was sick,
      named Lazarus, of Bethany,

Girl A: the town of Mary
      and her sister, Martha.

Girls: Therefore his sisters sent unto Jesus,
      saying

Girl B & Girl C: Lord,
      behold he whom thou lovest is sick.

Boys: When Jesus heard that,
        he said,

Boy 2: This sickness is not unto death,
        but for the glory of God,
        that the Son of God
        might be glorified thereby.

All: That the Son of God
        might be glorified thereby.

Girls: Now Jesus loved Martha,
        and her sister,
        and Lazarus.

Boys: When he had heard therefore
        that Lazarus was sick,
        he abode two days still in
        the same place where he was.

Boy 1: . . . and after that he saith

Boy 2: Our friend Lazarus sleepeth;
but I go,
that I may awake him out of sleep.

Boys: Then when Jesus came,
he found that Lazarus had lain
in the grave
four days already.

Girl B: Then Martha
as soon as she heard
that Jesus was coming,
went and met him:

Girl C: But Mary sat still in the house.

Girls: Then said Martha unto Jesus.

Girl B: Lord,
If thou hadst been here,
my brother had not died.
But I know
that even now,
whatsoever thou wilt ask of God,
God will give it thee.

All: God will give it thee.

Boy 1: Jesus saith unto her,

Boy 2: Thy brother
shall rise again.

Girl B: I know that he shall rise again
in the resurrection,
at the last day.

Boy 2: I am the resurrection,
and the life,
he that believeth in me,
though he were dead
yet shall he live:
And whosoever liveth
and believeth in me
shall never die.

All: And whosoever liveth
and believeth in me
shall never die.

Boy 2: Believest thou this?

Girl B: Yea, Lord:
      I believe that thou art the Christ
      the Son of God,
      which should come into the world.

Girls: And when she had so said,
      she went her way
      and called Mary her sister secretly,
       saying,

Girl B: *(whispering)* The Master is come
      and calleth for thee.

Girl A: When Mary was come where Jesus was
         and saw him,
         she fell down at his feet,
         saying unto him,

Girl C: Lord,
         if thou hadst been here
         my brother had not died.

Boys: When Jesus therefore saw her weeping,
         and the Jews also weeping
         which came with her,
         he groaned in the spirit
         and was troubled,
         and said,

Boy 2: Where have ye laid him?

Boys: They said unto him,
All: Lord, come and see.

Girls: *(sadly)* Jesus wept.

Girl C: Behold how he loved him!
Girls: Behold how he loved him!
All: Behold how he loved him!

Boys: Jesus therefore again groaning in himself
cometh to the grave. It was a
cave, and a stone lay upon it.

Boy 2: Take ye away the stone.

All: Then they took away the stone
from the place
where the dead was laid.

Boy 1: And Jesus lifted up his eyes,
and said,
Boy 2: Father I thank thee that thou
hearest me. And I knew
thou hearest me always;
but because of the people
which stand by I said it,
that they may believe
that thou has sent me.
All: That they may believe
that thou has sent me.

Boy 1: And when he thus had spoken,
he cried with a loud voice,

Boy 2: Lazarus, come forth.

All: *(quietly, like an echo)* Lazarus, come forth.

Girls: And he that was dead

All: *(joyfully)* came forth,

Girl A: *(with excitement)* bound hand and foot
with grave clothes
and his face was bound about
with a napkin.

Boy 1: Jesus saith unto them,

Boy 2: Loose him,
and let him go.

Boys: Then many of the Jews
which came to Mary

Girls: and had seen the things which Jesus did

All: believed on him.

One of a Kind

Bits and Pieces

"Made it!" Roger yelled as the soccer ball thumped against the side of the house. "Five goals in a row!" he said, tossing the ball to his friend, Pete. "Let's see you beat that!"

Just as Pete kicked the ball, Roger's dad turned into the driveway. He stopped the station wagon and got out. "Good kick, Pete," he called as the ball sailed across the yard. "You boys are getting pretty good!"

Pete grinned. "Thanks, Mr. Cord." He tucked the ball under his arm and followed Roger to the car.

"What's that, Dad?" Roger asked, peering into the big box Mr. Cord pulled from the back of the station wagon.

"Oh, just bits and pieces from different bikes," Mr. Cord answered. "I know a boy who needs a new bike. I thought I could put one together for him. You boys want to help?"

"Sure," the boys replied.

"How about carrying the box into the garage while I change into my work clothes?" asked Mr. Cord.

He opened the back door and went inside. The boys tugged the box into the garage and began to inspect the bike parts.

"Boy, your dad was right when he said they were from different bikes," said Pete. He held up a scratched fender. "This one is red and the other one is blue. Why would he want to go to all the trouble to put a bike together for someone else?"

"Dad is always doing things for someone else," replied Roger. "He goes with the pastor to visit people in town. When he meets someone who needs something, he tries to help."

"But why would he go to all the trouble of putting a bike together when he could just buy one?"

"Bikes aren't all that cheap," Roger replied. "I should know. I've been saving for a new one for almost a year."

Pete put the fender back into the box and looked up. "What kind do you want?" he asked.

Roger's eyes sparkled. "A Silver Streak," he replied.

"Wow!" said Pete. "No wonder you've been saving for a year. The Silver Streak is the best! How much money do you have?"

Roger sighed. "Not very much. I get an allowance, but I'm supposed to buy my school supplies out of that. It doesn't go very far."

The door slammed behind Mr. Cord. "Ready, boys?" he asked.

"What can we do?" Roger asked.

Mr. Cord took some pieces of sandpaper out of a box. "Why don't you sand the paint off the fenders?"

Roger pulled out a blue fender and Pete picked up a red one.

"I can get mine cleaner," challenged Pete.

"No, you can't," said Roger. The two boys went to work, rubbing as hard as they could.

An hour later Pete stretched and put down his tattered sandpaper. "I've got to go home," he said. "If I don't, I'll be late for supper."

"Thanks for the help, Pete," said Mr. Cord.

"See you later, Pete," said Roger. He walked with Pete to the garage door, and then came back to look at the bike frame his dad was putting together. "Think it's going to work, Dad?" he asked.

"Mm-hmm," Mr. Cord replied. "I think I have enough parts."

He stood up and wiped his hands. "Time for us to stop too."

Roger helped him put away the tools and clean up the garage before they went inside to eat.

The next afternoon Roger and Pete raced home from school on their bikes.

"Beat you!" Pete called, braking at the Cords' house.

Roger's wheels spun as he turned into the driveway. "Just wait," he frowned. "When I get my Silver Streak, I'll show you my dust!"

Pete just laughed. "Want to come over to my house?"

Roger glanced at the garage. The bike frame lay propped against the workbench.

"No," he said slowly, "I have to do my homework and then help Dad work on the bike when he gets home."

"Why? It's not your bike," Pete said.

"Dad wants me to help," Roger replied.

"Every day? Glad it's you and not me," called Pete as he pedaled away. "See you tomorrow."

When Mr. Cord got home, Roger was already in the garage, sanding the frame.

"Hi, Dad," he said, looking up.

His father grinned. "I'm glad to see you working already, Roger." He ran his hand lightly over the frame. "What do you think of it?"

Roger shook his head. "Well, it's no Silver Streak," he said. "But I guess if you don't have a bike . . ." His voice trailed off.

"Maybe you'll change your mind," Mr. Cord said cheerfully. "I'll change my clothes and be right out."

Do It Right

By suppertime the frame of the bike was almost free of paint. Roger put down the sandpaper and stretched. "I'm starving," he said.

Mr. Cord nodded. "You've done a fine job, Roger," he said. "This may take less time than I thought."

Tired as he was, Roger beamed at his father's praise. He helped put the tools away, and then they went inside the house. "Dad," he asked, "do I know the boy?"

"What boy?" His father reached for an old cloth and soap to wash his hands.

"The boy who gets the bike," Roger replied.

"Oh, that boy." Mr. Cord smiled at Pete. "Why don't you wait and see?"

Roger gave him a puzzled look, but Mr. Cord just smiled again and tossed a towel to Roger. "I thought you were starving," he said.

Roger wiped his hands hastily, the bike forgotten. "I sure am! Let's go!"

The next week Roger and Mr. Cord spent most of their afternoons in the garage. Mr. Cord worked slowly, taking care that each part was in good shape and fit perfectly.

"Why are you being so picky?" Roger asked when Mr. Cord rejected a part that looked fine to Roger.

"Son, if you want to do something . . ."

Roger grinned and finished, ". . . do it right!"

Mr. Cord laughed. "I guess I've said that a lot, haven't I?"

He wiped his hands as Roger nodded. "Well, this is for a special boy," Mr. Cord added.

"Special?" Roger looked up quickly, eyes gleaming with interest. "Still not going to tell me?"

"Nope." Mr. Cord reached in his pocket for his keys. "Why don't you clean these parts while I run down to the hardware store and pick up what I need."

"Okay, Dad," Roger said, "but one of these days I'll find out who that boy is!"

As Mr. Cord left, Pete rode up on his bike. "Hi, Roger. Still working?" he asked.

Roger stretched. "It's taking a long time to fix this bike. Where are you going?"

"Soccer practice," Pete replied. "You mean you're not going?"

Roger clapped his hand to his head. "I forgot!"

"Well, come on," Pete said. "We're going to be late."

Roger shook his head. "I can't. I told Dad I would clean these parts."

"Tell your mother you have to go to practice. She'll tell your dad when he comes back." Pete turned his bike around.

Roger hesitated. He hadn't played all week. What fun it would be to play with the other boys! Then he shook his head. "No, I'll wait until Dad comes back."

Pete gave a disgusted shake of his head. Roger stood still and watched him pedal down the street. Then he turned slowly back to work.

"This dumb bike," he grumbled to himself. "I wouldn't be surprised if it falls apart when that boy tries to ride it!"

Roger began to rub the metal. When his father came back the parts were almost clean, and Roger was ashamed of his anger. He and his father worked for another hour or so. Then Roger stood back to look.

"Hey, Dad," he said in surprise. "It looks like a real bike!"

Mr. Cord just grinned and began picking up his tools. Roger helped, stopping from time to time to look at the bike thoughtfully.

"You know something, Dad," he said as they closed the garage doors. "That bike would look pretty good painted blue."

Mr. Cord nodded. "Great minds think alike," he teased. "I picked up some blue paint at the hardware store. And some silver too."

"What's the silver for?" Roger asked.

"Oh, I thought you might want to decorate the bike some way," Mr. Cord said. "I'll leave that up to you."

After supper Roger could hardly wait to get upstairs to look through his books. He looked at picture after picture of bikes but couldn't find just what he wanted. Even the Silver Streak was no help. At last he picked up a pencil and paper and began to draw.

Lightning

The next afternoon Mr. Cord found Roger in the garage, paper and pencil in hand.

"Look at this, Dad." Eyes shining, Roger handed him the paper.

"This is good, Roger," Mr. Cord said slowly, looking from the paper to the bike. "And I think we can do it too! We'll have to be careful, though, to get it just right. As a matter of fact, after I spray the bike blue, you can paint the decorations yourself."

"Really?" Roger was delighted. "Thanks, Dad!"

He watched as Mr. Cord sprayed the bike frame. "How long will it take to put the rest of it together?" he asked eagerly.

"Not too long," his father replied. "Everything is ready. When this is dry, you can decorate it and we'll put it together.

Roger could hardly wait until the next afternoon. He raced home and charged upstairs to change his clothes. "I'll be out in the garage, Mom," he called, and raced out again. His mother opened her mouth to speak, then smiled and turned back to her work.

When Mr. Cord turned into the driveway, the bike frame was already painted. Silver handlebars glinted in the afternoon sunlight, silver racing stripes sparkled, and down the back fender a streak of silver lightning flashed against dark blue.

"It looks great, Roger!" Mr. Cord leaned forward to inspect the paint. "Neat job too. Is it dry?"

"Yes, sir," Roger replied, beaming. "May we put it together?"

"Sure thing. I'll be back in a minute."

When he came back outside, Mrs. Cord was with him. She stopped beside Roger and watched as Mr. Cord put the last parts on the bike. Then Mr. Cord stood up and steadied the bike on its kickstand.

"You two did a fine job," Mrs. Cord said. "That's the best bike I've ever seen!"

"Well, it's one of a kind," Mr. Cord said, smiling. "But I think it needs a name of its own, don't you, Roger?"

"Sir?" Roger took his eyes off the bike and looked at his father. "Oh, yes, sir. It has one—Lightning."

His father and mother looked at each other as Roger turned back to the bike. "Lightning? That's a fine name, son," said Mr. Cord. "Well, we're going in. Are you coming?"

"In a minute," Roger replied.

After they were gone, Roger walked around the bike. "One of a kind," he said to himself. "I wish . . ."

He shook his head and walked slowly to the garage door.

The next morning he was awakened by his father shaking his shoulder. "Wake up, son. It's Saturday. Time to deliver the bike!"

Roger groaned. "The boy!"

All through breakfast he struggled with his feelings. "I'm being selfish," he thought to himself. "Wanting a bike that Dad made for someone else!"

His feet seemed to drag as he followed his father to the garage. Lightning stood on its kickstand where it had been left. The early-morning sunlight picked out the silver sparkles as Mr. Cord wheeled it out into the driveway.

"Well, son, what do you think?" Mr. Cord asked.

"It's great, Dad." Roger swallowed hard.

"As good as the Silver Streak?" Mr. Cord sounded surprised.

Roger tried to smile. "Better, Dad. This bike is one of a kind, remember? Where are we going to deliver it?"

"It's been delivered, son," Mr. Cord said quietly. "It's your bike."

Roger stared. "Mine! But why didn't you say so?"

"Would you have wanted it at first?" Mr. Cord asked.

Roger shook his head, remembering how he had wanted a Silver Streak.

"We just couldn't afford a Silver Streak, Roger," Mr. Cord said. "I hope this one will do."

"It will, Dad, it will!" Roger gave his father a big hug.

Pete rode by, waved, and then stopped to look again. Roger looked at his father.

Mr. Cord chuckled. "Go ahead, son."

Roger hopped on the bike and spun out of the driveway. He braked beside Pete. Then wild whoops split the Saturday morning quiet as two bikes raced down the street.

What the Goodman Does Is Always Right

(Adapted from the story
by Hans Christian Andersen)

One Thing for Another

One morning the Goodman kissed his Goodwife good-bye and went off to town to sell their cow.

"Good-bye, my sweet," the Goodwife beamed. "I am sure you will make a good trade. Whatever you do is always right."

So the Goodman hiked up the long road to town, leading the cow all the way. On the road he met a man leading a goat.

"That is a fine goat you have there," said the Goodman.

"Aye, a fine goat indeed," came the reply. "And she can give you fine goat's milk and fine cheese."

The Goodman licked his lips at the thought of the milk and cheese. "Would you be willing to trade her for my old cow?" he asked.

"Aye, that I would," the man answered. And so the exchange was made. The Goodman was well pleased with his new goat. "The Goodwife will be happy," he said.

Now since the Goodman had made his trade, he wondered if perhaps he should go on home. But he was halfway to town now, so he decided he might as well go to see the sights.

On the way he met a man driving a hog in front of him.

"That is a fine hog you have there," said the Goodman.

"Aye, a fine hog indeed," came the reply. "And he would give fine pork chops and fine bacon to anyone wise enough to buy him." The Goodman's mouth watered at the thought of pork chops and bacon. "Would you be willing to trade him for this fine goat?" he asked.

"I would indeed," the man answered. And right then the exchange was made. The Goodman was well pleased with this new hog. "The Goodwife will be happy," he said.

"I must continue to town now," he said. "Who knows what other bargains I may find!"

On the way he met a man carrying a big tomcat.

"That is a fine tomcat you have there," said the Goodman.

"Aye, a fine tomcat indeed," came the reply. "And a finer mouse-catcher you have never seen. The mice are scared to come anywhere near the house where this tomcat lives."

The Goodman remembered that mice scurried around in the attic of his house. He tipped his hat and said, "Would you be willing to trade your tomcat for this fine hog?"

"I would indeed," the man answered. And so the exchange was made. The Goodman was well pleased with his new tomcat. "The Goodwife will be happy," he said, and he continued on his way.

Before long he met a man carrying a bag.

"What is in your bag?" the Goodman asked.

"These are flower seeds," came the reply. "And they will grow the prettiest daisies you have ever seen."

The Goodman smiled at the thought of pretty daisies. "Would you be willing to trade the seeds for this fine tomcat?" he asked.

"I would indeed," came the reply. And before you know it, the exchange was made. The Goodman was well pleased with his new flower seeds. "I am sure the Goodwife will be happy," he said.

What Will She Say?

Before much longer the Goodman reached the town. Two fine-looking gentlemen came up to him. "What have you brought to trade?" they asked.

"Oh, I have already done all my trading," answered the Goodman. And then he told them how he had traded the cow for the goat and the goat for the hog and the hog for the tomcat and the tomcat for the flower seeds. "And I am sure that the Goodwife will be pleased," he finished.

"Pleased!" one of the men exclaimed. "More likely she will fly into a rage and never let you hear the end of it. Imagine taking a cow to town and coming back with only a bag of flower seeds!"

"Nevertheless," said the Goodman, "the Goodwife will be pleased. She is pleased with every trade that I make. Whatever I do, she says, is always right."

"This is something we must see," said the second of the two men. "And if it is true that she does not fly into a rage but kisses you instead, we will give you a bag of gold."

Now this sounded like an agreeable idea to the Goodman, so he invited the two gentlemen home with him.

"We will not go inside," said one man, "for your wife may act differently in front of company. We will peek in and listen at the window."

"As you like," said the Goodman. When the two gentlemen were settled outside of the window, he went inside.

The Goodwife ran to greet him. "How did the trade go in town, my dear?" she asked.

"Oh, as well as could ever be, my darling," her husband replied. "On the way to town I passed a man leading a goat, and he agreed to trade her for my cow."

The Goodwife swished her skirt and pranced across the room. "Oh, wonderful," she exclaimed. "Now we can have goat's milk and goat's cheese every day."

"But then I traded the goat for a hog," said the Goodman. The Goodwife clapped her hands for joy. "How delightful!" she exclaimed. "Now we can have pork chops and crispy bacon to eat."

"But then I traded the hog for a tomcat," said the Goodman. The Goodwife lifted her hands into the air. "Better and better!" she exclaimed. "Now we can get rid of the mice in the attic that keep us awake at night."

"But then I traded the tomcat for a bag of flower seeds," said the Goodman.

The Goodwife threw her arms around her husband and kissed him. "That is the very best of all," she said. "For no matter how dreary our days become, we can have smiling flowers at our doorstep, ready to wish us well. I knew that you would do the right thing."

As she spoke, the two finely dressed gentlemen entered the house. "You were true to your word," they said to the Goodman. "And here is your bag of gold. But a wife like this one is worth far more than any gold we could ever give you."

The Goodman thanked the two gentlemen, and the Goodwife invited them to stay for supper.

And how do you suppose the Goodman spent the gold? Well, he may have bought a cow or a goat or a tomcat or even some more seeds. But whatever he did with it, you may rest assured that it was *always* right.

Thanksgiving Day

Over the river and through the wood,
To grandfather's house we go;
 The horse knows the way
 To carry the sleigh
Through the white and drifted snow.

Over the river and through the wood—
Oh, how the wind does blow!
 It stings the toes
 And bites the nose,
As over the ground we go.

Over the river and through the wood
 Trot fast, my dapple-gray!
 Spring over the ground,
 Like a hunting-hound!
 For this is Thanksgiving Day.

Lydia Maria Child

What to Do?

At eight o'clock Saturday morning Annabelle woke up. The raindrops spattering against the window seemed to be teasing her.

"Can't go out and play today! Can't go out and play today! Plip, plop, plip, plop, plip, plop."

Annabelle pressed her nose against the windowpane. "It doesn't seem fair somehow," she muttered. With a deep sigh, she padded over to the bed where her sister Margaret still lay asleep.

"Hey, Margaret, wake up!" she whispered. She shook Margaret twice, jumped up on the bed, and sat down on top of her.

"Ugh." Margaret rolled over and looked at Annabelle through half-closed eyes. "Go away."

"It's Saturday," said Annabelle, as if that were the reason she was there. "But we can't go outside because it's raining."

"Rain on Saturday!" Margaret snorted with disgust. "Oh, brother."

Annabelle made a face and bounced off Margaret's bed. She hopped up and down on her old box springs and talked in quick breaths between hops.

"Harvey and I were going to play mudballs. But mudballs don't work when they're that wet. Too squishy-squashy-wishy-washy." And she bounced down onto her bed in a heap.

"It's probably just as well," Margaret yawned as she dangled her legs over the side of the bed. "Mudballs is a silly game."

"Mudballs is a perfectly good game," Annabelle answered stoutly. "It's just not very good on rainy days. Now I won't have anything to do today."

She pressed her nose against the windowpane
again, thinking about mudballs.

She thought about
what fun it was to let
the mud splash on Harvey.

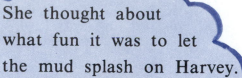

She thought about what
fun it was for Harvey to
splash the mud on her.
She thought about spraying
each other under the hose
and running around in the
hot sun to dry.

She sighed. "What will we
do-do-do, me and you-you-you?"
she whispered in a singsong voice.

"Don't press your nose against the glass,"
Margaret answered. "It gets the glass all messy."

Annabelle pretended she hadn't heard. "I smell
bacon. Sizzlin', frizzlin' bacon and c-o-f-f-e-e
boiling in a pot. Mama and Papa must be up."

"Breakfast!" said Margaret. "Come on! I'm as
hungry as a bear."

Annabelle made a face. "That's silly," she said.

After breakfast Papa leaned back in his chair and took a long drink of coffee. "Well, what are you two going to do today?" he asked.

"Some friends and I were supposed to have a bike race," Margaret answered. "But we can't now. It looks like it's going to rain all morning and all afternoon."

"And all night," Annabelle continued in a gloomy voice, "and all tomorrow and all the next day and all. . ."

Mama said, "Annabelle, if you think hard, you can find something fun to do inside the house. Have you used your bright little mind?"

"No, Mama, I just felt sad because I couldn't play mudballs with Harvey."

Margaret gave the last half of her toast to Annabelle. "Mama, as soon as I'm finished with my chores, I'm going to read, if that's all right. I like to read when it's raining. It feels cozy."

"Big sisters always have books to read," Annabelle muttered. "I've already read all mine . . . twice."

Margaret said, "There's a book on my nightstand you can read. It's easy enough for you."

Annabelle bumped up the stairs backwards. "I've probably already read it," she said.

When Margaret came up, Annabelle was just finishing the book. She slapped the page. "I knew it," she said. "I just knew that the little girl with the golden curls would eat all his porridge."

"Well, I'm going to read now, Annabelle," said Margaret. "My book is really exciting. Please get off my bed."

Annabelle slowly went back downstairs. "Mama, I don't have anything to do," she said.

"Well, that isn't really a problem, Annabelle." Mama spoke in a cheery voice.

"You can think of something. Just try to use your brain."

"I'm not sure I have one," replied Annabelle gloomily.

Mama got out a pencil and some paper. "There's no telling what you can come up with when you put your mind to work," she said, handing the paper and pencil to Annabelle. "Go into the den to think in peace."

Something to Do

Almost as soon as Annabelle was seated at the table, she wrote *Annabelle, Annabelle.* She scrunched up her nose and looked at the words. Then underneath that she quickly wrote *Tumbled down a wishing well.*

"Well, it's kind of funny," she sighed. "But I don't think it'll be a very good poem."

She thought some more. Then she wrote again.

> Saturday, Saturday
> Ploppy-pitter-patter day
> Doesn't-really-matter day
> Saturday.

Annabelle mused, "It doesn't make much sense. I think it needs a second verse."

> Rainy day, rainy day
> Water-down-the-drainy day
> Try-to-use-your-brainy day
> Rainy, rainy day.

Annabelle sighed again and carefully folded the paper seven times until she couldn't fold it again, no matter how hard she tried.

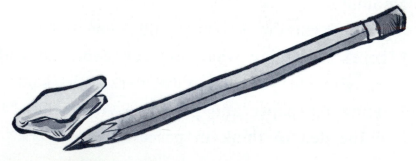

"Annabelle, look who's here," Mama called. Harvey came padding into the den with his yellow rubber boots, his yellow slicker, and his bright yellow umbrella.

"Harvey!" Annabelle called. "I'm just about to write a story, and you can help me."

"Oh, boy!" Harvey hopped to the table. "What's it about?"

"I think it's about all of us, but mainly me. You can help me write it. We have to draw pictures for it too."

She and Harvey settled down to work. They talked about the story they wanted to write. Then they wrote and drew and colored until they had written and drawn and colored all they could. When they were finished, they put the pages together. This is what the story looked like:

Once upon a time Annabelle and Harvey didn't have anything to do.

So they decided to take a rocket trip to the moon.

Then they went for a picnic in the park.

They took a trip across the sea.

They went to visit Grandma Bear.

All this story writing and drawing took
Annabelle and Harvey quite a while. When they
finished, Mama came in to look at their work.
"This is excellent work," she said. "I can see you
spent a lot of time on it. And—" she picked up
the folded paper and unfolded it—"I like your
poetry, dear."

Annabelle blushed and smiled.

Papa came in and read the story. "This is great, Annabelle and Harvey!" he said. "And you said you had nothing to do."

Margaret came in and read their story too. "This is almost as good as the book I just finished reading," she said.

"I knew you could use your bright mind to help the time pass," Mama said. "Look out the window."

Annabelle and Harvey looked out the window. The sun had begun to shine. They looked at each other. Then Annabelle shouted, "Last one out is a giant mudball!" Together they raced out the door.

The Trail West

The following story is a fictional account of the Lincolns' move from Indiana to Illinois. The incident involving Abe Lincoln's rescue of the little dog is true.

A rabbit dashed out of the woods and down the hill, followed by a yapping little dog. With a flick of his tail, the rabbit disappeared down a hole. The little dog trotted around the hole, sniffing. Then again yapping loudly, he began to dig. One ear perked up as he heard children's voices calling in the woods; then he returned to his frantic digging.

"Dog!" a voice called sternly. A tall, lanky young man strode out of the woods. He stopped

beside the little dog and looked at the wet dirt scattered around the hole. "Dog," he scolded, shaking his head. "You've been chasing rabbits again. One of these days you're going to get left behind!"

Scooping up the dog, the young man called, "Here he is!"

"Abe found him!" The shout was repeated again in the woods. "Abe found him!"

Soon Abe Lincoln's young nephews and nieces were gathered around him, out of breath from running.

"Chasing rabbits again," said one of the boys, trying to frown at the muddy dog wriggling in Abe's long arms.

"Let me hold him, Abe. I'll keep him from chasing rabbits," said one of the girls.

Abe handed his little dog to his niece. "Now, you mind this time, dog," he scolded. "No more trouble from you!"

"Here come the wagons," he said. The children looked up as Abe's father drove the first wagon over the top of the hill. The canvas top swayed as the oxen pulled hard in the mud. Mr. Lincoln cracked his whip and called to the oxen, "Come on, boys!"

Mrs. Lincoln held on to the edge of the wagon seat as they started down the hill toward Abe and the children. Two other wagons followed, those of Dennis Hanks and Levi Hall, Abe's brothers-in-law. Abe's sisters called to their children as the wagons stopped.

"Will we camp here for the night?" Dennis Hanks asked Mr. Lincoln.

"It's a good place," Mr. Lincoln replied, looking around.

Mrs. Lincoln stepped down from the wagon, wrapping her shawl tighter around her. "Looks like Abe's dog found us a camping place," she said, smiling at Abe.

"He picked a good one," Abe said, nodding toward a stream close by. "There is fresh water."

Abe helped the men unhitch the oxen. Then they went into the forest with their long rifles. It was not long before they came back with a wild turkey. Soon the smoky smell of roasting turkey brought hungry children crowding around the campfire.

Mr. Lincoln thanked God for taking care of them on their long trip across Indiana. Then the cold and weary travelers ate until they were full.

When he was finished, Mr. Lincoln stretched his legs. "Well, I'm tired, but I'm still glad to leave Indiana. This has been a hard winter for us."

"Just think of spring in Illinois," sighed Mrs. Lincoln. "I hope we can plant apple trees."

"We might if you'll bake your apple pies," teased Dennis.

"I hope the farmland is as good as everyone says it is," Levi said. He moved closer to the fire to warm his hands. "Land that does not have to be cleared sounds fine to me. We'll still have time to plant crops this spring."

"And the game! Deer and bear and everything else! We'll have plenty to eat," Dennis laughed. "We might even be able to fatten up Abe!"

Abe laughed with the others. His little dog stretched and yawned as Abe rubbed it behind the ears.

"You are right, little dog," said Abe. "It is time for bed."

The next morning the little dog licked Abe's face. Abe opened his eyes. "All right, all right," he said sleepily. "Out you go."

He climbed out of the wagon and set the little dog down. Abe looked around. Ice covered the puddles of water and hung from the tree branches.

"Spring's not here yet, dog," Abe sighed.

The little dog sniffed the frosty air as he trotted toward the woods. Suddenly a rabbit hopped out of the grass in front of him and dashed between the wagons. With a happy yelp, the chase was on.

Abe laughed as the rabbit stayed just ahead of the little dog.

Across the camp they went, back and forth.

Then the dog ran too close to the campfire. He bumped the forked branches that held Mrs. Lincoln's pot.

Ashes scattered everywhere, and the pot fell down over the dog.

Heads popped out of the wagons. "What is all that racket?"

"Somebody get that dog out of my pot!" called Mrs. Lincoln.

Abe lifted the pot and picked up the little dog.

"See what I told you," he laughed. "Leave those rabbits alone!"

With everyone awake, the day's work began. By sunup the wagons were ready to move again. Ice cracked under the oxen's feet as they plodded along. Wagon wheels creaked as they rattled west toward Illinois.

Abe and the children walked beside the oxen. The little dog trotted behind them. As the sun rose higher in the sky, the ice melted and made puddles. In the afternoon the wheels of the Lincolns' wagon stuck. The oxen strained and pulled, but the wagon didn't move.

The other men stopped their wagons to help. They cut branches and dragged small logs from under the trees and packed them under the wheels.

Abe got on the wagon seat.

"Hi, Hi! Come on, boys," he shouted. The oxen pulled hard, but still the wagon didn't move.

"Wait, Abe," called his father. "Dennis and Levi will help me push behind the wagon."

As the three men pushed, Abe cracked the whip, shouting to the oxen. The little dog ran under the wagon and nipped fiercely at the oxen's heels. The oxen snorted and pulled. The wheels creaked and the wagon began to move.

"Come on, boys," shouted Abe.

The wagon jerked and mud splashed everywhere. They were out of the hole! The three men wiped mud from their faces.

Abe laughed as he jumped down from the high wagon seat. "I had the best job," he said.

His father picked up the muddy little dog. "Your dog almost got stepped on," he said. "Better put him in the wagon."

Abe cleaned the dog as well as he could before putting him in the wagon. "Stay there, dog. We have work to do."

That was not the last mudhole on the trail.
The travelers went through another and another as
spring rains swept the country. The cold and wet
sent the children huddling under the canvas. At
night the puddles were frozen; the next day the
sun melted the trail into slush. But everybody was
happy. They were going west! The closer they got
to Illinois, the more they wanted to go on.

Then one day they came to a stream they
couldn't cross.

"Do you think we can make it across with the
wagons?" Dennis asked, looking at the ice-covered
water.

Mr. Lincoln shook his head doubtfully. "It looks dangerous," he said. "Let's see if there is a shallow spot upstream or downstream."

The men walked both directions and looked. There was no better place to cross. They returned to the wagons where their wives waited. The children were playing on the bank, the little dog running at their heels.

"We'll have to cross here," Mr. Lincoln told the women. "Better get the children into the wagons."

Quickly the children climbed into the wagons, sitting close to their mothers. They made no sound as the wagons creaked one by one into the water. If the wagons tipped over, everything could be lost!

The thin ice cracked under the oxen's feet.
Water rushed around their legs.

"Easy, boys," cried Abe's father as the wagon
swayed. The wagon bumped slowly along as the
oxen felt their way carefully. At last they were on
the other side of the stream.

"Good boys," called Abe as he and his father
jumped down. Abe led the oxen out of the way
as the other two wagons splashed by them.

"Look, Uncle Abe," called one of the boys, leaning out the back of a wagon. "There is your little dog!"

Abe looked back across the stream. Sure enough, there was the little dog! He was dashing back and forth on the other side.

"Why didn't someone put him in the wagon?" asked Levi.

Abe groaned. "I thought the children had him."

"He wasn't with us when we got into the wagons," called one of the girls. "Probably chasing rabbits again!"

"Dog, I told you you'd get left someday," Abe called. "Over here, come over here!"

The little dog whined and looked down at the broken ice, then looked back at Abe.

"He's afraid of the ice, Abe," said his stepmother. "He won't swim."

"We can't help him now," said Mr. Lincoln. "We can't take a wagon back across that stream. It's too dangerous."

"Abe, we've got to go on," said Dennis kindly. "It'll be dark shortly."

One of the girls began to cry. Abe looked at the little dog.

"The wagons can't go back across, but a man could," he said thoughtfully.

He sat down and began to pull off his shoes and socks.

"You'll catch your death of cold," cried Mrs. Lincoln.

"I can't leave him there to die," Abe replied as he stepped into the water. Slowly he felt his way through the rushing water. The thin, broken ice swept past his legs. Halfway across the stream he slipped. The people on the shore gasped, but Abe caught himself and moved on, still feeling his way with his bare feet.

When he reached the other side, the happy dog met him, wagging his tail. Abe picked him up and looked across at the other shore. It would be even harder going back. How would he keep the dog still?

Abe thought for a moment, then tucked the dog into his shirt. The little dog lay still as Abe began the crossing again. Slowly, foot by foot, he felt his way through the freezing water. His feet grew numb, until he could barely feel the rocks under them. At last he reached the other shore. The men pulled him up on the bank, and Mrs. Lincoln quickly wrapped him in a blanket.

"Had us worried there for a minute, Abe," Levi said.

"Into that wagon, Abe Lincoln," his stepmother said tearfully. "You're soaked to the skin!"

Abe obeyed quickly. His stepmother was right. His feet felt like chunks of ice. He pulled the blanket around him and hugged the shivering dog.

"You had better give up rabbit hunting for awhile," he said to the little dog. "I wouldn't like to do that again soon!"

The little dog whined and looked up at him. Then he yapped once as if in agreement and curled up next to Abe.

The Beast of the Desert

Wild Horse Canyon

Leather creaked as Orly shifted in his saddle. One of the ranch hands turned to look at him. "Tired?" Slim asked, grinning at Orly. "When I was your age, I could ride fifty miles without getting off my horse. Why, one time. . ."

Orly grinned as Slim launched into one of his tall tales. Tired? On his first wild horse roundup? Orly thought of all the times he had begged to come and had been told that he was not old enough. He straightened in his saddle, easing the growing stiffness in his legs.

The men had been riding since before dawn. Last week a rancher had told Grandpa that a red stallion had been seen in the canyons bordering the desert. They had never gone this far on a roundup before, but Grandpa said that this particular stallion and his band of mares were worth riding miles for.

The red-rimmed canyons ahead of them were
outlined against the bright sun, their rocky walls
glowing pink and orange. The men slowed their
horses, looking for signs of the wild horses. Seeing
none, they rode into the canyons. Orly craned his
neck, staring up at the rocks towering above him,
almost forgetting about the wild horses.

Grandpa turned down another canyon, holding his hand up for quiet. Orly held his breath but heard nothing. When Grandpa motioned, they rode on and entered an arroyo.

"A stream! and grass!" Orly said, surprised.

"This is why the stallion is bringing his mares here," Grandpa said, inspecting the rocky walls carefully. "Here," he said, pointing to an opening in the rocks. "A dry wash."

At Orly's questioning look, Grandpa explained, "Used to be part of the stream. It's dried up now. We can block it off, drive the horses into it, and capture the whole band."

He turned to Slim. "Slim, climb up on those rocks and keep an eye out for the stallion and his mares."

"Grandpa, may I . . ." Orly began.

Grandpa grinned. "Can you use some help, Slim?"

"Why sure," Slim replied. "Got another story to tell anyway."

Orly followed Slim, matching handholds up the rocks. At the top they lay on a huge flat rock, looking out over the desert.

Slim had almost finished his tale when a trail of dust appeared on the horizon.

"Here they come!" Slim pushed his hat back on his head and grinned at Orly. "I can't wait to get my saddle on that red stallion. What a ride we'll have!"

Orly peered over the edge of the rock and shaded his eyes against the glare of the sun. "Aw, you can't see that far, Slim," he said.

"Why, you had better believe I can, son. Just wait and see."

Orly watched the trail of dust drift skyward as it moved closer. At last he could see the band of wild horses, manes flowing as they galloped toward the arroyo.

"Let's get moving," said Slim. Orly backed away from the edge of the rock, and they scrambled down.

"The horses are coming, Grandpa!" Orly called. "Are you ready?"

Grandpa looked up from the tangle of mesquite branches he and the cowboys had used to block the dry wash. He shoved the last branch into place and wiped his face.

"About as ready as we'll ever be," he said to the excited boy. "Mount up, partner!"

"Hurry, Grandpa. They might leave before we get there!" Orly urged.

"Hold on there, Orly," laughed Grandpa. "That red stallion brought his mares down for water and grass. They're in no hurry to leave."

As he and Orly swung into their saddles, Grandpa called to the cowboys.

"Make sure you get the horses turned into the dry wash. That stallion is a smart one. He won't give us another chance."

"Sure thing, Mr. Sloan," Slim said, laughing. "The animal that can outsmart Old Slim here hasn't been born!"

Orly and Grandpa rode their horses around to the mouth of the arroyo. The band of horses had finished drinking and were grazing along the stream.

"Beautiful, aren't they?" Grandpa pointed to the leader of the band. The stallion's red coat was easy to spot among the darker mares. "He's the one we need to head off. The others will follow him."

"Let's go, son," said Grandpa. They spurred their horses out from under the trees. Yelling and waving their hats, they rode toward the band of horses.

The red stallion reared and galloped away, his mares close behind him. They splashed through the shallow water and raced toward the dry wash.

"Hi-ee!" yelled Orly, waving his hat in the air. Through the dust he saw Slim and the others gallop out in front of the racing horses. Then he saw another dim shape appear behind the waving men. A roar from the strange creature echoed in the canyon.

As Slim turned to look behind him, the wild horses swung into the dry wash. They skidded to a halt at the blocked end. Then with a wild rush, the stallion headed back through the opening.

"Stop them, boys!" shouted Grandpa. He and Orly urged their horses faster, trying to close the gap.

But the cowboys were having trouble. Their horses were jumping and bucking, trying to get away from a large animal.

Grandpa swung his horse around, pushing Orly's pony out of the way as the wild horses swept past them. Orly's eyes filled with tears as they disappeared around the bend.

"We've lost them, Grandpa," he cried.

Grandpa didn't answer. He was staring at the huge, dirty beast trotting through the dust. It had long, thin legs and a curved neck. It held its head high and looked down its long nose at them.

Slim galloped up, swinging his rope. "Let's see what this thing is," he said. The rope looped neatly over the strange animal's neck.

The animal jerked its head back and spat. Slim dropped the rope and wiped his wet face.

"Dirty beast!" Slim scrubbed and scrubbed his face. The animal turned and trotted away into the dry wash.

"Throw those mesquite branches across the gap," Slim called to the other cowboys. The animal moved slowly about as they blocked the way out of the makeshift corral.

"What is it, Grandpa?" asked Orly.

"Well, Orly," replied Grandpa, "I think it's a camel."

"A camel!"

The Broncbuster

Orly climbed on the rocks to get a better look at the camel.

"It does have a hump, Grandpa. But where did it come from?"

Grandpa rubbed his chin. "The army brought some camels to America about fifteen years ago. They were going to use them in the desert. Nothing ever came of it, though."

Slim stuffed his handkerchief back into his pocket. "Didn't they just turn them loose in the desert when the Civil War started?"

"That's what I heard," Grandpa replied. "Though some were used in traveling animal acts. This one probably hasn't been loose too long. It's not very scared of us."

One of the cowboys looked sideways at Slim. "That's one four-legged beast you can't ride," he said slyly.

"Slim can ride anything! You can ride him, can't you, Slim?" asked Orly.

"Why, sure, Orly," Slim said. "It's a four-legged animal like any other one. Too bad we don't have a saddle to fit him."

"Slim, you've been bragging that you can ride anything big enough to hold you, saddle or bareback," said the cowboy. "This one's big enough to hold you all right."

The cowboy jumped down and grabbed the end of the rope. "Here you go," he grinned, and tossed it to Slim.

"Ride him, Slim!" called Orly.

Slim climbed down into the dry wash. "How do I get on?" he asked.

"Lead him over to that big rock," suggested Grandpa. "You can try jumping on him."

Slim didn't look too happy, but he climbed on the rock and pulled on the rope. When the camel was close enough, he took a deep breath and jumped.

The camel stepped sideways, and Slim sprawled flat in the dust. The men roared with laughter and slapped their legs.

Slim staggered to his feet and looked at the camel. The camel stared back at Slim.

"I'm not through with you yet," Slim muttered, climbing back on the rock.

"Wait a minute, Slim," called Grandpa. "Put this through the hole in his nose."

He tossed Slim a long piece of leather. When Slim looped it through the camel's nose, he was able to pull the camel closer to him. Again he jumped. This time he landed on the camel's hump. For a moment it looked as if he had made it. Then he slowly slid over the other side. It was seven feet to the ground. Slim hit hard. For a moment he lay quietly. Then he crawled to his feet and brushed himself off.

His critics shouted encouraging remarks which Slim stubbornly ignored.

"Grandpa," said Orly, "the stories in my schoolbook say camels always kneel to let the riders get on. Can we pull him down for Slim?"

"Good idea, son," said Grandpa. He climbed over the rocks. Two of the other cowboys jumped down into the corral. Together they pulled the protesting camel to its knees.

"Hop on, Slim," the cowboys shouted. Slim climbed on the camel's hump. Clutching the leather strap in one hand and holding on with his knees, he waved his hat and said, "Let go!"

In one swift movement, the camel unfolded its long back legs. Slim flew over the camel's head.

"Good ride, Slim!" The men slapped each other on the back.

"This is no picnic, you know," Slim snapped as he crawled to his feet. "I'd like to see you try it!" He shook his hair out of his eyes and glared at the long-legged beast. "Pull him down," he said.

The men brought the camel to its knees again. Slim climbed back on the hump. This time he pulled the strap tight with both hands and braced his feet on either side of the camel's neck.

"Let go!" he yelled again.

This time when the camel lurched to its back feet, Slim braced himself against the camel's long neck. Then the camel unfolded its front legs and stood up. Slim clung tightly to the strap, swaying with the movement of the camel.

"He did it!" yelled Orly.
The men cheered.

Slim grinned from ear to ear. "It's all in knowing how," he said smugly.

"Can we take it home, Grandpa?" Orly asked eagerly.

"Well, it sure isn't what we came for," said Grandpa. "There's not a chance of catching the wild horses now. But won't the folks be surprised," he chuckled at the thought. "Can you ride it home, Slim?"

Slim swayed back and forth as he rode the camel around the corral. "Sure can, Mr. Sloan."

It was a strange crew riding through the canyons on the way home. Slim rode far ahead of the still nervous horses. As the camel topped the crest of the hill, it was outlined against the setting sun.

"Look, Grandpa!" said Orly. He pointed to the camel and its rider.

Grandpa shook his head. "Who would have thought of it? A camel in America!"

GLOSSARY

This glossary has information about selected words found in this reader. You can find meanings of words as they are used in the stories. Certain unusual words such as foreign names are included so that you can pronounce them correctly when you read.

The pronunciation symbols below show how to pronounce each vowel and several of the less familiar consonants.

ă	pat	ĕ	pet	î	fierce
ā	pay	ē	be	ŏ	pot
â	care	ĭ	pit	ō	go
ä	father	ī	pie	ô	paw, for

oi	oil	ŭ	cut	zh	vision
ŏŏ	book	û	fur	ə	ago, item,
ōō	boot	*th*	the		pencil, atom,
yōō	abuse	th	thin		circus
ou	out	hw	which	ər	butter

a·bode | ə **bōd'** | —*verb*   Stayed or remained in the same place.

ac·ro·bat | **ăk'** rə **băt** | —*noun*   A person who is skilled in performing on a trapeze, walking a tightrope, and tumbling.

a·dapt | ə **dăpt'** | —*verb*   To change or adjust to fit different conditions.

A·has·u·e·rus | ă **hăz** ŭ **ē'rŭs** | —*noun*   King of Persia, married to Esther.

air·craft car·ri·er | **âr'** krăft **kăr'** ē ər | —*noun*   A large ship that is part of a navy and is used as an air base.

Ant·arc·ti·ca | ănt **ärk'tĭ** kə | or | ănt **är'** tĭ kə | —*noun*   The continent surrounding the South Pole. It is almost completely covered with ice.

ap·par·el | ə **păr'** əl | —*noun*   Clothing, especially outer garments.

arch | ärch | —*verb*   To make or cause to make an arch; curve or bend.

arch·bish·op | ärch **bĭsh'** əp | —*noun*   A bishop of the highest rank.

ar·roy·o | ə **roi'** ō | —*noun*   A deep gully cut out by a stream that comes and goes with the rains; dry gulch.

as·sure | ə **shoor'** | —*verb*   **1.** To say positively; declare. **2.** To make certain; guarantee.

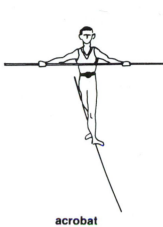

acrobat

B

bard | bärd | —*noun*   A singing poet who composed and recited verses about history and legends.

bee·line | bē′ līn | —*noun*   A direct, straight course.

big top | bĭg tŏp | —*noun*   The main tent of a circus.

blub·ber | blŭb′ ər | —*noun*   The thick layer of fat under the skin of whales, seals, and some other sea animals.

budge | bŭj | —*verb*   To move or cause to move slightly.

busi·ness | bĭz′ nĭs | —*noun*   The work a person does for money; a job or occupation.

chanter

clavier

C

can·yon | kăn′ yən | —*noun*   A deep valley with steep cliffs on both sides and often a stream running through it.

cease | sēs | —*verb*   To bring or come to an end; stop.

chal·lenge | chăl′ ənj | —*verb*   l. To call to take part in a contest or fight. **2.** To call for a person's efforts and skills.

chant·er | chăn′ tər | —*noun*   The pipe of a bagpipe on which the melody is played.

chron·i·cle | krŏn′ ĭ kəl | —*noun*   A chronological record of historical events.

cla·vier | klə vîr′ | or | klā′ vē ər | —*noun*   A stringed keyboard instrument.

ă	pat	ĕ	pet
ā	pay	ē	be
â	care	ĭ	pit
ä	father	ī	pie
î	fierce	oi	oil
ŏ	pot	oŏ	book
ō	go	ōō	boot
ô	paw,	yōō	abuse
	for	ou	out
ŭ	cut	zh	vision
û	fur	ə	ago, item,
th	the		pencil,atom,
th	thin		circus
hw	which	ər	butter

304

colo·nel | kûr′ nəl | —*noun* An officer in the Army, Air Force, or Marine Corps. A colonel ranks above a major and below a general.

com·pa·ny | kŭm′ pə nē | —*noun* A subdivision of a military unit, usually under the command of a captain.

com·pos·er | kəm pō′ zər | —*noun* A person who composes, especially a creator of musical works.

con·fi·dence | kŏn′ fĭ dəns | —*noun* Trust or faith.

con·fu·sion | kən fyōō′ zhən | —*noun* Mixed-up excitement.

con·nec·tor | kə nĕk′ tər | —*noun* A machine piece that joins other parts of the machine together.

con·tri·bute | kən trĭb′ yōōt | —*verb* To give or supply; donate.

cor·ral | kə răl′ | —*noun* A pen or a place with a fence for keeping cattle or horses.

cour·age | kûr′ ĭj | or | kŭr′ ĭj | —*noun* A quality of mind or character that makes a person able to face danger or hardship without fear or in spite of fear.

court·yard | kôrt′ yärd | or | kōrt′ yärd | —*noun* An open space surrounded by walls or buildings.

coy·o·te | kī ō′tē | or | kī′ ōt | —*noun* A North American animal that looks somewhat like a wolf. Coyotes are common in the western part of the United States and Canada.

coyote

crit·ic | krĭt′ ĭk | —*noun* A person who is able to judge others in a certain area.

dap·ple-gray | dăp əl-grā′ | —*noun*   A horse with a gray coat with darker gray spots or markings.

darning floss

darn·ing floss | därn′ ĭng flôs | —*noun*   A soft, loosely twisted thread used to mend a hole in clothing.

de·but | dā byōō′ | or | dā′ byōō | —*noun*   A first public appearance, as of an actor.

de·cree | dĭ crē′ | —*noun*   An official order; a law.

de·liv·er | dĭ lĭv′ ər | —*verb*   **1.** To carry and give out, such as a letter. **2.** To release or rescue; set free.

din | dĭn | —*noun*   Loud, confusing noise.

dis·tress | dĭ strĕs′ | —*noun*   Serious danger or trouble.

drawl | drôl | —*verb*   To speak slowly.

drone | drōn | —*verb*   To talk in a boring, dull way.

drum·roll | drŭm′ rōl | —*verb*   To beat a drum in a continuous series of very short blows.

dry wash | drī wŏsh | —*noun*   The dry bed of a stream.

eb·on·y | ĕb′ ə nē | —*noun*   The hard, black wood of a tree that grows in the tropics.

ex·pe·di·tion | ĕk spĭ dĭsh′ ən | —*noun*   A long trip, usually for exploring or studying something not known or far away.

ă	pat	ĕ	pet
ā	pay	ē	be
â	care	ĭ	pit
ä	father	ī	pie
î	fierce	oi	oil
ŏ	pot	ŏŏ	book
ō	go	ōō	boot
ô	paw,	yōō	abuse
	for	ou	out
ŭ	cut	zh	vision
û	fur	ə	ago, item,
th	the		pencil, atom,
th	thin		circus
hw	which	ər	butter

ex·per·i·ment | ĭk spĕr′ ə mənt | —*noun*
Something done to show a fact, test a theory,
or find out what might happen.

fire pan | fīr păn | —*noun*   A container to hold
the fire in a hot-air balloon.

flat·ter·y | flăt′ ə rē | —*noun*   Insincere praise.

flinch | flĭnch | —*verb*   To pull back quickly in
pain or fear; wince.

flur·ry | flûr′ ē | —*noun*   A sudden outburst;
a stir.

fringe | frĭnj | —*noun*   An edge made of
hanging threads or cords.

fire pan

gal·lant | găl′ ənt | —*adjective*   Brave and
good; courageous.

gal·lows | găl′ ōz | —*noun*   A frame from
which criminals are hanged. The typical
gallows is made of two upright posts with a
beam across them. A noose is tied to the beam.

Gem·i·ni IV | jĕm′ ə nī | or | jĕm′ ə nē |
—*noun*   Fourth spacecraft in the Gemini series.
The astronauts aboard were James McDivitt
and Edward White.

glint | glĭnt | —*noun*   A momentary flash of
light; sparkle.

glis·ten | glĭs′ ən | —*verb*   To shine by
reflection.

glo·ri·fy | glôr′ ə fī | or | glōr′ ə fī | —*verb*
To give glory, honor, or high praise to; exalt.

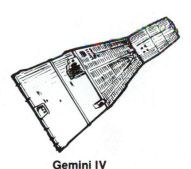

Gemini IV

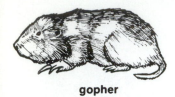

gopher

iceberg

good·man | go͝od′ mən | —*noun*   The male head of a household; master.

go·pher | gō′ fər | —*noun*   A small North American animal that has pouches like pockets in its cheeks. Gophers live in burrows that they dig in the ground.

graze | grāz | —*verb*   To feed on growing grass.

guf·faw | gə fô′ | —*noun*   A loud or rude burst of laughter.

guid·ance | gīd′ ns | —*noun*   Help or advice; counsel.

H

halt | hôlt | —*noun*   A stop; a pause.

har·ness | här′ nĭs | —*noun*   Gear used by astronauts to keep them safe during liftoff and in free fall.

head·wa·ters | hĕd′ wŏ tərs | —*noun*   The water from which a river rises or begins.

Herr | hĕr | —*noun*   A German title of respect, similar to the English *Mister*.

hip·po·drome | hĭp′ ə drōm | —*noun*   An oval track made especially for horses.

hy·dro·gen | hī′ drə jən | —*noun*   A gas that is very light and that burns easily. Hydrogen is one of the chemical elements.

I

ice·berg | īs′ bûrg | —*noun*   A very large mass of floating ice in the ocean. An iceberg is a piece of a glacier that has broken off and can be very dangerous to ships.

ă	pat	ĕ	pet
ā	pay	ē	be
â	care	ĭ	pit
ä	father	ī	pie
î	fierce	oi	oil
ŏ	pot	o͝o	book
ō	go	o͞o	boot
ô	paw,	yo͞o	abuse
	for	ou	out
ŭ	cut	zh	vision
û	fur	ə	ago, item,
th	the		pencil, atom,
th	thin		circus
hw	which	ər	butter

in·ter·rupt | ĭn tə **rŭpt′** | —*verb* To break in upon something that someone is saying or doing.

in·ves·ti·gate | ĭn **vĕs′** tĭ gāt | —*verb* To examine carefully in a search for facts, knowledge, or information.

i·vo·ry | **ī′** və rē | —*noun* The smooth, hard, yellowish white material that forms the tusks of elephants and certain other animals.

J

jes·ter | **jĕs′** tər | —*noun* In the Middle Ages, a person kept by kings, queens, and other nobles to entertain or amuse them.

jester

jour·nal | **jûr′** nəl | —*noun* A daily record of events.

K

kilt | kĭlt | —*noun* A pleated, plaid skirt that reaches down to the knees. Kilts are worn by men in Scotland.

knight | nīt | —*noun* A soldier in the Middle Ages who served and pledged loyalty to a king or lord.

knight

L

lank·y | **lăng′** kē | —*adjective* Tall, thin, and clumsy.

lar·i·at | **lăr′** ē ĭt | —*noun* A long rope with a sliding noose at one end, used especially to catch horses or cattle; lasso.

lariat

Lat·in | **lăt′ ĭn** | —*noun* The language of the ancient Romans.

lute | lo͞ot | —*noun* A stringed musical instrument with a body shaped like half a pear with a long, bent neck. It is played by plucking the strings.

mesquite

M

ma·jor | **mā′ jər** | —*noun* An officer in the Army, Air Force, or Marine Corps who ranks above a captain.

me·nag·er·ie | mə **năj′** ə rē | or | mə **năzh′** ə rē | —*noun* A collection of live wild animals on exhibition.

mes·quite | me **skēt′** | or | **měs′** kēt | —*noun* A thorny shrub or tree of southwestern North America. It has feathery leaves and long, narrow pods.

me·zu·zah | mə **zo͞oz′** ə | —*noun* A small piece of paper with the verses from Deuteronomy 6:4-9 and 11:13-21 written on it and marked with the word *Shaddai*, a name of the Almighty. It is rolled up in a small box and nailed to the door frame of a home as a sign that a Jewish family lives there.

miffed | mĭfd | —*adjective* To have one's feelings hurt.

mill·ing | **mil′** ĭng | —*verb* Moving around in a confused way.

mim·ic | **mĭm** ĭk | —*verb* To copy; imitate.

mis·judge | mĭs **jŭj′** | —*verb* To be wrong in judging.

mezuzah

ă	pat	ĕ	pet
ā	pay	ē	be
â	care	ĭ	pit
ä	father	ī	pie
î	fierce	oi	oil
ŏ	pot	o͝o	book
ō	go	o͞o	boot
ô	paw,	yo͞o	abuse
	for	ou	out
ŭ	cut	zh	vision
û	fur	ə	ago, item,
th	the		pencil,atom,
th	thin		circus
hw	which	ər	butter

mourn | môrn | or | mōrn | —*verb* To feel or show sorrow or grief for a death or a loss.

Mo·zart | mō′ tsärt | —*noun* A world-famous musician who wrote many pieces of music and mastered the violin and piano while still a child.

mus·ket | mŭs′ kĭt | —*noun* An old gun with a long barrel. Muskets were used before the invention of the rifle.

musket

mus·tang | mŭs′ tăng | —*noun* A small, wild horse of western North America.

must·y | mŭs′ tē | —*adjective* Having an old, stale, or moldy smell or taste.

muz·zle | mŭz′ əl | —*noun* The projecting part of an animal's face that includes the nose and mouth; snout.

nav·i·ga·tor | năv′ ĭ gā tər | —*noun* A crew member who plans and directs the course of a ship or an aircraft.

mustang

no·tice | nō′ tĭs | —*verb* To become aware of.

op·er·a | ŏp′ ər ə | or | ŏp′ rə | —*noun* A musical play in which most of the words are sung to orchestral music.

or·bit | ôr′ bĭt | —*noun* The path that a manmade satellite or spacecraft takes around the earth.

muzzle

or·phan | ôr′ fən | —*noun* A child whose parents are dead.

penguin

peony

ă	pat	ĕ	pet
ā	pay	ē	be
â	care	ĭ	pit
ä	father	ī	pie
î	fierce	oi	oil
ŏ	pot	ŏŏ	book
ō	go	ōō	boot
ô	paw,	yōō	abuse
	for	ou	out
ŭ	cut	zh	vision
û	fur	ə	ago, item,
th	the		pencil,atom,
th	thin		circus
hw	which	ər	butter

ox·y·gen | ŏk′ sĭ jən | —*noun* A gas without color or smell. Oxygen is one of the chemical elements. It makes up one-fifth of the air. People and animals need oxygen to live.

P

pa·tri·ot | pā′ trē ət | or | pā′ trē ŏt | —*noun* A person who loves, supports, and defends his or her country.

Pe·cos Bill | pā′ kŏs bĭl | —*noun* The main character in a Western cowboy legend.

peer | pîr | —*verb* To look closely in order to see something clearly; stare.

pen·guin | pĕng′ gwĭn | —*noun* A sea bird with webbed feet and narrow wings that look like flippers. Penguins cannot fly, but use their wings for swimming. Many penguins live in or near Antarctica.

pe·o·ny | pē′ ə nē | —*noun* The large pink, red, or white flowers of a garden plant.

pi·geon | pĭj′ ĭn | —*noun* A bird with short legs, a plump body, and a small head. Pigeons are common everywhere, even in cities.

Pike's Peak | pīks pēk | —*noun* A mountain in the Rocky Mountains of Colorado.

plains | plānz | —*noun* A large, flat area of land without any trees.

por·ridge | pôr′ ĭj | or | pŏr′ ĭj | —*noun* A thick cereal or soup made by boiling oatmeal, beans, peas, or other grains in water or milk.

post | pōst | —*verb* To put announcements up in a place or in several places for everyone to see.

312

pow·der horn | pou′ dər hôrn | —*noun*   A container for gunpowder. A powder horn is made of an animal's horn with a cap or stopper at the open end.

prance | prăns | —*verb*   To rise on the hind legs and spring forward.

pre·serve | prĭ **zûrv′** | —*verb*   To protect; keep in safety.

quest | kwĕst | —*noun*   A search, especially for something valuable.

range | rānj | —*noun*   A large area of open land on which livestock graze freely.

reb·el | **rĕb′** əl | —*noun*   One who rejects authority or fights against it.

reed | rēd | —*noun*   A thin strip of wood used in the mouthpiece of certain wind instruments. The reed vibrates when air passes over it and produces a musical tone in the instrument.

re·gion | **rē′** jən | —*noun*   Any large area of the earth's surface.

rein | rān | —*noun*   A long leather strap attached to the bit in a horse's mouth and held by the rider or driver to control the horse.

res·ur·rec·tion | rĕz ə **rĕk′** shən | —*noun*   The act of rising from the dead or returning from the dead.

re·treat | rĭ **trēt′** | —*verb*   To fall back before an enemy attack; withdraw.

rein

313

scepter

snowshoes

ă	pat	ĕ	pet
ā	pay	ē	be
â	care	ĭ	pit
ä	father	ī	pie
î	fierce	oi	oil
ŏ	pot	ŏŏ	book
ō	go	ōō	boot
ô	paw,	yōō	abuse
	for	ou	out
ŭ	cut	zh	vision
û	fur	ə	ago, item,
th	the		pencil,atom,
th	thin		circus
hw	which	ər	butter

ret·ro·rock·et | rĕt′ rō rŏk′ ĭt | —*noun* A rocket engine used to slow, stop, or turn the motion of an aircraft, missile, spacecraft, or other vehicle.

ring·mas·ter | rĭng′ măs tər | —*noun* A person in charge of the performances in a circus ring.

Rome | rōm | —*noun* The capital of Italy.

roost | rōost | —*noun* A place where birds settle to rest or sleep. —*verb* To rest or sleep on or in a roost.

rud·der | rŭd′ ər | —*noun* Something on a ship or plane that controls direction; guide.

S

Sab·bath | săb′ əth | —*noun* The seventh day of the week, which God commanded the Jews of the Old Testament to observe as a day of rest.

sack·cloth | săk′ klôth | or | săk′ klŏth | —*noun* A rough cloth of camel's hair, goat hair, hemp, cotton, or flax. Garments made of this cloth were worn as a symbol of mourning.

sav·age | săv′ ĭj | —*noun* A primitive or uncivilized person.

scep·ter | sĕp′ tər | —*noun* A rod or staff that is held by a king or queen. It is a symbol of authority.

scur·ry | skŭr′ ē | —*verb* To run or move about quickly.

snow·shoe | snō′ shōō | —*noun* A light, racket-shaped frame strung with strips of leather or rawhide. Snowshoes are worn under the shoe to keep the feet from sinking into snow.

314

spec·ta·tor | spĕk′ tā tər | —*noun* Someone who watches an event but does not take part in it.

spir·its | spĭr′ ĭts | —*noun* **1.** A person's mood or state of mind. **2.** Enthusiasm, courage, or pep.

spin·dle | spĭn′dl | —*noun* A rod or pin on a spinning machine that holds and winds the thread.

spin·ning frame | spĭn′ ĭng frām | —*noun* A machine that pulls and twists fibers into yarn and winds the yarn on spindles.

spinning frame

spin·ning jen·ny | spĭn′ ĭng jĕn′ ē | —*noun* An early type of spinning machine that had several spindles.

spool | spōol | —*noun* A small cylinder made of wood, metal, or plastic. Thread and wire are wound around spools.

spool

stalk | stôk | —*verb* To move in a quiet, cautious way so as not to be noticed; steal after.

St. Ber·nard | sānt bər **närd′** | —*noun* A very large dog of a breed that was once used to help travelers in the mountains.

tal·ent | tăl′ ənt | —*noun* A natural ability to do something well. Although talent is something a person is born with, it almost always has to be developed with study and practice.

St. Bernard

ta·ter | **tā′** tər | —*noun*   A short, slang way to say "potato."

taunt | tônt | —*verb*   To tease, mock, or jeer at someone.

thick·et | **thĭk′** ĭt | —*noun*   A dense growth of shrubs or small trees.

thresh | thrĕsh | —*verb*   To separate the seeds or grain from a plant by striking or beating it.

un·der·take | ŭn dər **tāk′** | —*verb*   To decide or agree to do.

u·ni·cy·cle | **yōo′** nĭ sī kəl | —*noun*   A vehicle made of a frame built over a wheel and usually propelled by pedals.

unicycle

Val·ley of Jez·reel | **văl′** ē ŭv **jĕz′** rĭ ĕl | —*noun*   Valley located about fifty-five miles north of Jerusalem.

Vi·en·na | vē **ĕn′** ə | —*noun*   Capital of Austria.

whin·ny | **hwĭn′** ē | or | **wĭn′** ē | —*verb*   To make a gentle neighing sound.

wid·ow | **wĭd′** ō | —*noun*   A woman whose husband has died and who has not remarried.

wine·press | **wīn′** prĕs | —*noun*   A vat in which the juice is pressed from grapes.

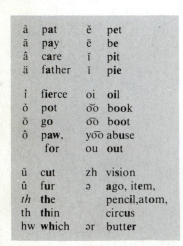

ă	pat	ĕ	pet
ā	pay	ē	be
â	care	ĭ	pit
ä	father	ī	pie
î	fierce	oi	oil
ŏ	pot	ŏŏ	book
ō	go	ōō	boot
ô	paw,	yōō	abuse
	for	ou	out
ŭ	cut	zh	vision
û	fur	ə	ago, item,
th	the		pencil, atom,
th	thin		circus
hw	which	ər	butter